When the author's book, "Killing Cancer" was first written, he didn't have the authorization to include the names of some very important people around the world that had helped him tremendously. Now, eighteen years later, he has that permission. The author wishes to thank:

HRH Prince Charles

The Archbishop of Canterbury

Prince Tawan Ku of Borneo

Prince Obazee of Nigeria

Mr. Hashimoto,
Health Minister of Japan

Ruth Montgomery,
author and ex-White House correspondent

Josef de Ubaldo,
famed herbalist, author and lecturer

Jaime Licauco,
psychic researcher, television and radio personality, author and friend of manila.

A Personal Letter from Sir Jason Winters

I want to thank you for reading this book. Because of people like you, the world is changing. It has become obvious to all of us that medical science alone cannot solve all of our modern day maladies. Ancient remedies will not replace modern medical breakthroughs, but, as we are finding out quickly, they can certainly help tremendously.

Ancient and natural therapies have been tried out over the centuries and the ones found to be effective are still in use today.

Seventy-five years ago in England, for example, my Grandmother, "Grandma Lewis" was busy helping distressed people by giving them St. Johns Wort. Now, millions know that this herb works every bit as good as the modern day prozac, with one big difference however—St. Johns Wort does not have any side effects and no withdrawal symptoms.

In 1920, Grandma Lewis was giving a mixture of garlic, gensing and ginger to the survivors of World War I who were suffering from shell shock, depression and shattered nerves. Her close relative, Lord Lewis, was on her health herbal formulas every day *while serving in the British Parliament*.

So, now you and I are aware that all healing arts must work together for the benefit of all. There can no longer be bitterness and hatred between orthodox and alternative practitioners. The time has come for open minds, more understanding and more compassion for all.

Since 1977, when I should have died, some very important people have helped me and I would be remiss not to thank them.

To Prince Charles, who placed his hand on my shoulder and said, "Don't worry Mr. Winters, only God can tell you when you will die."

To the Archbishop of Canterbury, who, with Christian love took time from his busy schedule to research the herb referred to so many times in the Bible.

To Dr. Ian Pierce who tested the herbal tea formula in the laboratory.

To Dr. Malcolme Rae, who gave me such courage and strength.

To U.S. Congressmen James Bilbray and John Ensign for the award they gave me.

Thanks to Health Minister Hashimoto of Japan, Jaime Licoaco of the Philippines, and to Josef de Ubaldo of Manila, head of the Herbalist Association.

To Ruth Montgomery, America's favorite author.

And, finally, to the United States Surgeon General, for his invaluable report on antioxidants.

The author wishes to make it clear that he does not recommend total rejection of orthodox methods of treating illness, or a doctor's advice. If you are ill, see your doctor and tell him that you will do whatever he feels that you should. Then ask him if its all right if you change your diet to a more sensible one, and if he minds if you take herbs or herbal combinations. Any thinking doctor will see no problem with this.

Sir Jason Winters' objective is to get all of the healing arts, both orthodox and unorthodox, natural and chemical, to work together for the benefit of mankind.

He follows the instructions of Prince Charles who stated at a grand opening of the Bristol Clinic, "We must all work together to help our fellow man."

The Jason Winters Story

by Benjamin Roth Smythe

Vinton Publishing

1st Printing 1990 — 10th Printing 1996

This book contains © material from the following books:

1st Printing 1980—102nd Printing 1997

1st Printing 1983 — 24th Printing 1997

1st Printing 1986 — 22nd Printing 1997

1st Printing 1984 — 30th Printing 1997

1st Printing 1996— 3rd Printing 1997

ISBN: 1885026-06-4 New Retail Price $19.95

Published by:
VINTON PUBLISHING INTERNATIONAL CO.
P. O. BOX 94075, LAS VEGAS, NEVADA, 89193
(800) 897-9747 • FAX (702) 739-0461
INTERNET ADDRESS: http://www.sirjasonwinters.com
PRINTED IN THE U.S.A.

England

The rain had been falling lightly all day long on the small brick house in Hove, Sussex. The house was a city-owned, subsidized rental unit. In the small bedroom on the second floor, a baby was about to be born, while a few close relatives waited anxiously. "It's a boy," the midwife stated calmly. He was named Raymond Winters. A few moments later, the child's grandfather arrived. He was a tall, strange man of few words. He crossed over to the bed, looked at the newborn and stated, "He will be nothing more than a cat burglar." (In the English terms, cat burglar means someone who climbs onto roofs and into windows to rob people.) With that, he walked out. He never spoke to the child or the mother again. Twenty-seven years later, and thousands of miles away, famous actor Audie Murphy, accompanied by Raymond Winters, walked across the desert to sit down next to an old Indian actor. The movie these men were making' was being shot in old Tucson, Arizona, where most "B" westerns were made for Universal Studios of Hollywood. It was titled "*Walk the Proud Land*," a movie in which Raymond had his first acting job. The three men made themselves comfortable around the campfire. They were soon joined by Jay Silverheels who played Tonto of Lone Ranger fame, and the beautiful Patricia Crowley. As they sat quietly, the old Indian startled everyone by suddenly saying in a very loud and strong voice, "You are far from a cat burglar now!! Your grandfather wants you to know that he is proud of you and says he is sorry for the way he acted at your birth." Of course, no one around the fire knew what that meant. No one, that is, except for Raymond Winters. It took him months to get over the shock of that statement. While growing up, his family had teased him about the "cat burglar" statement many times. The grandfather had died some twenty years prior to the making of this movie. This book is about Jason Raymond Winters. He was born in strange surroundings with very weird things occurring. This strangeness, this protection, this psychic aspect has stayed with him always, even to this day.

Introduction

Jason Winters is one of the most remarkable human beings that I have ever known—a soul from the spirit plane who willingly exchanged places with a dying Hollywood stunt man in order to benefit humanity. Bringing in with him an awareness of ancient herbal remedies he completely rejuvenated the cancer-ridden body that he now occupies, and has gone on to heal many thousands of others of cancer and other maladies.

The herbal remedies that he developed are now being utilized throughout the world, and as a result he has been knighted by several countries. He gives freely of himself and is much sought after throughout Asia, Europe and the United States, as a lecturer on herbs, diet and general health.

I have no financial interest whatsoever in his endeavors, but am a deep admirer of the qualities within him that can serve as a lodestar for all of us in our own quest for spiritual advancement.

He is a "walk-in" par excellence!

Ruth Montgomery
Author, "Threshold to Tomorrow"

TABLE OF CONTENTS

THE FEDERATION OF INTEGRATED MEDICINE

(Operating Worldwide)

The Federation for Integrated Medicine has as its purpose the comprehensive integration of complimentary and orthodox medicines. This will be achieved by the attainment of tyhe following objectives.

TO PROMOTE and support scientific resarch into complementary medical treatments and their integration with orthodox medical treatments;

TO PROMOTE wider awareness of the clinical and economic benefits of effective integrated health and medical practices, both among health care professionals and in the wider community;

TO COLLECT, codify, disseminate and thereby protect the knowledge of complementary medical practices and treatments for the benefit of future generations of practitioners;

TO COLLABORATE with other medical and complementary organizations thus benefiting from all sources of knowledge.

THE OBJECTIVE is to get all of the healing arts, both orthodox and alternative, to work together for the benefit of mankind.

Sir F.R.J. Winters K.G.S.J.
President

1940 - LOST IN LONDON

It was England 1940. German aircraft would attack London every night—most people spent their nights in air raid shelters. The town of Brighton, situated on the south coast of England, bore the brunt of most raids, as the Luftwaffe had to fly directly over that town on their way to London, the city that Adolph Hitler had promised to flatten. Children were being evacuated from Brighton and sent to the center of England, a place considered safe at that time.

One of the children boarding the bus to safety was ten-year-old Jason Winters. Each child carried a small paper bag full of clothes and an extra pair of shoes with laces tied, hanging around their neck. Jason's father was the one to see him off as his mother was busy working at the large Harrington's Aircraft Factory. Jason recalls that his father kissed him. He had never done that before, nor was he ever to do that again. But for all of his life the child remembered that kiss. Jason Winters was tall for his age and so towered over the other students. This, of course, made him the brunt of many jokes. The bus unloaded at the town of Birstall in Leicstershire. The two female teachers in charge of this particular group of children had a list of families who had volunteered to take care of a child for the duration of the war. And so it started. At two p.m., the fourteen children and two teachers walked the streets dropping off children. The pretty little girls were the first to be chosen, then the smaller boys. At six p.m. the teachers were worried. All the children had been placed in good homes except for this tall, skinny boy named Winters. Time and again, people would look at this "giant" and say, "No, we want a girl." At last they knocked on the door of number 33 Fielding Road, the home of Mr. and Mrs. Freestone. They were middle aged, had no children, and certainly did not want to open their doors to this gangly lout. But they were persuaded. From the first day, Jason sent desperate letters home. Letters written on toilet paper and with no stamps on the envelope. They were delivered nevertheless. "I must come home," the letters pleaded. "I will walk if

I have too. Please don't leave me here!"

The postman delivering the letters to Jason's parents felt almost as badly as they did. After four terrible months of extreme unhappiness, Jason's mother told Mrs. Freestone to put the boy on a train for London's Euston Station. She would pick him up there, then travel across London to Victoria Station, and take the train back to Brighton. On the way to Euston Station, a German bomb fell on the railway tracks. The train was delayed for many hours. Arriving in London, Jason's mother was no where to be found. With tears in his eyes he waited and waited, then, decided to walk across the city to Victoria Station. He had fifteen shillings in his pocket, enough to purchase a ticket to Brighton. During the long walk, there was an air raid. Jason ended up in the arms of a policeman who took him to a shelter. He was shocked to learn that this child was walking across London by himself. He bought him a cup of tea and a cheese sandwich. He then directed the child to Victoria Station. Upon arrival, Jason saw his mother sitting on a bench crying and wrought with fear at not being able to find her son. It was a great reunion. Jason was happy again.

1952-1957 — Lumberjack to Movies

It was below zero in the lumber camp in Tahsis, British Colombia. Jason was working on the worst job that anyone could get—pulling on the green chain. As the logs were sawn into planks, they came down a conveyor belt. Jason's job was to pull them off and stack them up into piles. The stacker would then carry them away. On this job, if you stopped for a instant, the planks would pile up and a person could never catch up again with the constant flow of lumber. Jason felt that he should leave. He had six hundred dollars in the bank and had not had a vacation in years. At twenty two, he needed some excitement, so that same evening, after collecting his pay, he boarded a Greyhound bus bound for Vancouver. He longed for the warm sunshine and so purchased a second ticket to Guaymus, Mexico. The trip was long, but worth it. He stayed in a cheap hotel on the beach, lay in the sun all day, swam and fished. Every evening he would go to the cantina and drink and dance and every evening would end up with a different, but beautiful, senorita. After one month, he found that he was down to his last twelve dollars. At least he had his return bus ticket. So he climbed onto a bus bound for Tucson, Arizona. The wait-over for the bus to Vancouver was eight hours. To fill in time, Jason went to the Five Star Santa Rita Hotel, not to check in, but just to sit in the comfortable lobby and wait. He noticed dozens of people dressed up in old western garb, and Indians with buckskins and war paint, all milling around the lobby. A well-dressed, elderly man came over to Jason and demanded that he stand up, turn around.

Jason thought that he must be the hotel manager until the man asked, "How much do you weigh? How tall are you? Can you ride a horse?" Jason answered the man and was immediately led to the coffee shop where three other gentlemen were sitting. "What do you think of him?" the man asked them while pointing at Jason. It turned out that the men and all the people in the lobby were making a movie for Universal Studios. Audie Murphy was the star and Patricia Crowley the starlet. The men had mistakenly thought that Jason was waiting for an interview to become an extra in the movie. He was hired and for the next three weeks earned eighty dollars each day along with room and board. His job was to be the stand in for Jay Silverheels, the famous Indian actor. From this Indian he found the secret to blood purification. In this movie, titled "Walk the Proud Land," Jason did all the riding, fighting and stunts for the famous "Tonto."

1967

It is the Canadian Centennial and Jason Winters was asked to do something spectacular to celebrate. The tall gangly boy had immigrated to Canada with his family and had been lumberjack in British Columbia. He and a friend decided to travel the Great McKenzie River, from the Great Slave Lake, sixteen hundred miles down to Inuvik, on the

Arctic ocean. With canoe loaded, the two men pushed away from the dock, with the press and Indians cheering them along. It was a long, hard trip. Bitten by insects constantly, the two men traveled in the absolute silence of the seventh largest river in the world. One day the canoe was badly damaged by a great north storm.

Tremendous winds, torrential rains, the canoe was filling with water quickly. They pulled ashore and lay soaking wet and exhausted, while the thousands of insects bit them incessantly. Three days they were stranded on this beach, many miles from civilization, with no roads or trails to follow. Jason built a fire in a cave and the two men actually prepared to starve to death. An R.C.M.P. helicopter saw the smoke and landed on the beach. The pilot, who had been told to look out for the two men, strapped the canoe to the float of his helicopter and flew the two filthy and hungry men to a secret oil exploration camp. They were greeted like brothers, fed beans and steaks, then put to bed in a small hut to sleep for ten hours. Upon awakening, they found that the exploration people had completely repaired the canoe. Jason insisted on the helicopter returning them to the exact spot on the river that he had found them so they could resume and complete their trip. The newspapers were full of these stories as the two worked their way successfully down to the Arctic Ocean.

1968

Jason had purchased a hot air balloon, called it "Oh Canada" and was training with the department of transport to obtain some kind of balloonist pilot license. This was difficult as no one had ever obtained such a license before. After weeks of perseverance, he at last received it. He was going to be the first man to fly across the Rockies by balloon. He soon found out why no one else had ever tried it. Updrafts would swirl the balloon up to fourteen thousand feet, then drop it down so low that the gondola was scraping the tops of the mountains. At eight thousand feet, the balloon was free falling when a freak wind turned the balloon into a sail. It crashed at a speed of thirty-miles-per-hour. Knocked unconscious, he lay for at least an hour. Then he started to walk out over the lush terrain. After three hours of walking,.. a jeep pulled up. The driver, Mr. Ralph Nichols, quickly took Jason to the hotel in High River where he was treated like royalty. A local seamstress sewed the balloon and in two days time, he took off to finish the planned trip.

1969

Across the Atlantic by Helium Balloon. Arrangements were being made for an Englishman to be the first man to cross the Atlantic by balloon. Jason was everyone's first choice, for by now the media was stating that "this guy will try anything." With a helper, Jason placed the giant balloon into a trailer and drove across Ontario and on to Halifax, Nova Scotia. He had arranged for a large truckload of helium cylinders to be delivered to take off spot.

Helium, being lighter than air, causes the balloon to rise. The take off day arrived. Thousands were there to see this spectacular event. The balloon was filled with helium, the wind was westerly, which was how it had to be. A nun rushed up to the boat that the two men were sitting in and pressed the holy cross into Jason's hand. Then, amidst a thousand cheers, the balloon lifted skyward and was away. Jason had done away with the traditional gondola and had replaced it with a small sailing boat, a fact that was to save the lives of the two-man crew. Late that night, drifting along in complete silence and darkness they heard the sound of engines. A plane roared past them, circled, then shone a very bright searchlight on the balloon. They heard a voice over the loud speaker shout "Good luck, Jason," then the plane disappeared. They were to find out later that the voice belonged to Prime Minister Trudeau. He had taken the time to fly out to wish them luck. Over the Marconi radio, the two men could keep in touch with the world, until, quite suddenly, they could hear violently crashing waves. Jason checked the altimeter and found that they were losing altitude rapidly. They had to lose weight. They threw over all kinds of equipment, but still lost altitude. At last they threw overboard the Marconi radio. This slowed down the decent, but they still crashed amid thirty foot swells. The balloon had to be cut lose quickly, otherwise the small boat would overturn. Jason watched the twenty-thousand-dollar balloon disappear across the sea. It now lies somewhere at the bottom of the Atlantic. Two days later, with no land in sight, and quite sea sick, an air-sea rescue plane spotted them when Jason raised the yellow sail to attract their attention. A fishing boat was dispatched to pick up the men. The mission had failed. But the two men survived.

THE JAGUAR

A brick wall had been built across the road. It was made of cinder bricks and cement. It was ten feet high and twelve inches thick. A ramp had been built on one side. On the other side was a panel van. The police were controlling the crowds of onlookers. The paramedics were in place as well as the emergency fire department. Jason's job—to drive a Jaguar car at 40 miles-per-hour down the road, up the ramp and smash into the brick wall. The object—to test the new safety belts for automobiles. Every news media was there. The starter lowered the flag as a signal for Jason to begin, and, with the crowd gasping, he sped down the road and up the ramp crashing through the brick wall and demolishing the panel van on the other side. Parts of the wall had flown over fifty feet spraying the area with debris. A fire started in the rear of the Jaguar as firemen rushed to free Jason from the wreckage. After what seemed an eternity he stepped out of the vehicle in perfect condition. Seat belts were made mandatory in New Zealand.

Book One

And Now. . .

Terminal Cancer

Special Notice

Since the Jason Winters story became known throughout the world, many authors have written about it. This book, however, is the only authorized version. Full permission and cooperation were given to Benjamin Roth Smyte to write this accurate account of an astounding event.

Sir Jason Winters story as seen on television shows "SIGHTINGS," "Strange Universe," radios "London Calling," "Voice of America," "Radio India," "Singapore News," Philippines "Wake Up Call." Sir Jason is also the subject of 17 books and numerous news and magazine articles.

Vinton Publishing
Las Vegas, Nevada

INTRODUCTION

When Jason Winters first contacted me to write about his experiences I was very busy with other work, and even though he was calling from the U.S.A., I tried to put him off. He was quite persistent, however, and finally I had him send me the manuscript for my perusal. Within a week a package arrived consisting of cassette tapes entitled "The Jason Winters Story." I started to listen to them with complete disinterest, then sat up and began to take notice. Something in this man's voice portrayed sincerity and great compassion.

His claims about cancer, herbs, laetrile, world travel, and ultimate health, if true, were something the world should know about without delay.

First, though, I had to check out his story, the hospital, doctors, x-rays, cancer clinic, Dr. Malcome Rea of Great Britain, and the others. Then I started to check his source of information, starting with the Bible, the writings of Buddha, Krishna, Bihii Ulla, and Hippocrates. Everything I found verified Winters' story.

The research to check took me six months, and then I informed Winters that I would indeed write this book ("Killing Cancer") for him. As always, I wrote it in the first person.

And so, dear readers, I give you "The Jason Winters Story." May it be an inspiration to all who read it.

Benjamin Roth Smythe
Author, Scientific Writer and Chemist

PROOF OF TERMINAL CANCER

IN THE UNITED STATES DISTRICT COURT FOR THE
WESTERN DISTRICT OF OKLAHOMA

GLEN L. RUTHERFORD, et al.,)
Plaintiff,)
vs) No. CIV-75-0218-B
UNITED STATES OF AMERICA,)
Defendant.)

PHYSICIAN'S AFFIDAVIT FOR PATIENT'S
IMPORTATION AND USE OF LAETRILE

I, (Name) ABEL MELLADO, of (Address) PASEO NOMUMENTAL I/A (City) TIJUANA, (State) BAHA CAL, do hereby swear and affirm that the following facts are true and accurate:

1. That I am a practicing physician (M.D.), licensed to practice medicine in the State of Baja California, Mexico.

2. That I have conducted a thorough medical examination of (Name) F.R.WINTER, (Address) 1265 BARCLAY ST, (City) VANCOUVER, (State) CANADA on (Date) JULY 28th 19 77 who has cancer of the (body location) TONSILS.

3. That it is my professional opinion that the histological evidence of the above-named cancer patient demonstrates a rapidly progressive malignancy possessive of a high and predictable mortality rate. The above-named patient therefore is presently a terminally ill cancer patient.

4. I further affirm that based upon my professional opinion and knowledge of the facts concerning the above-named patient: [Check one of the following]

- [ ] a. that further orthodox treatment would not reasonably be expected to benefit the patient; or
- [ ] b. that laetrile will be administered only in conjunction with established and recognized forms of cancer treatment; or
- [x] c. that the patient has made a knowing and intelligent election to take laetrile after being fully apprized of the full range of recognized treatments available and of the fact that laetrile is considered by most cancer experts to be of no value in combatting the disease.

Any injectable laetrile will be administered only under the supervision of a doctor (M.D.).

Dated this 28 day of July, 19 77.

[signature]

STATE OF California)
COUNTY OF San Diego)

Subscribed and sworn before me this 28th day of July 19 77.

My Commission expires: NOTARY PUBLIC M A Figueroa

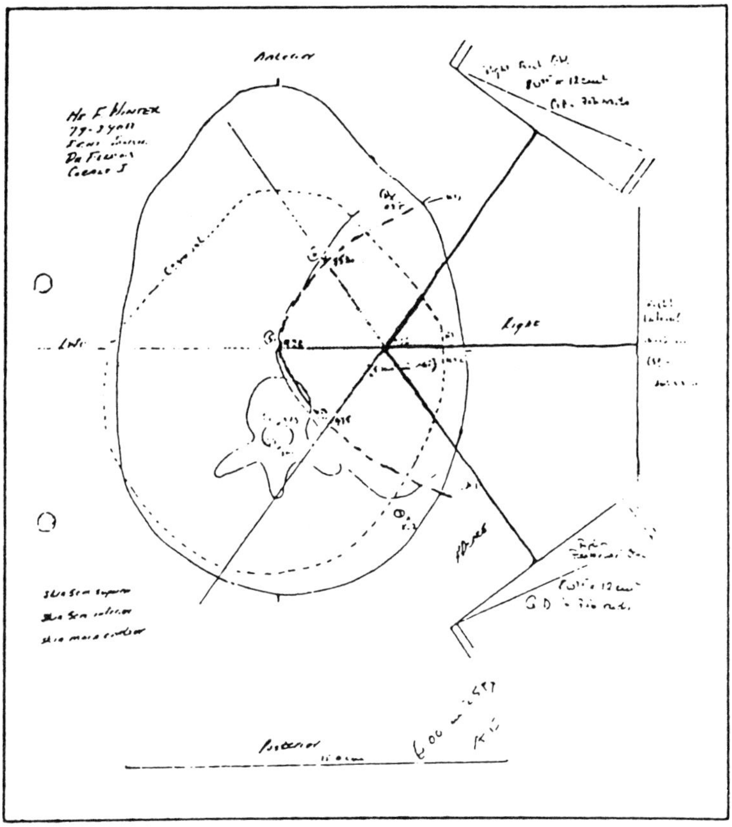

This is a medical drawing of Jason Winters' head based on actual X-ray photos. The view is from the top of the skull looking down. The shaded area marks the tumor.

When I was twelve, my father gave me two dollars to memorize this poem. It has had a profound effect on my life. I asked him if we could include this wonderful work in the book—he agreed. May this poem by Rudyard Kipling inspire you, the reader, as it has inspired me, my entire life.

Raymond Winters

IF —
Rudyard Kipling (1856 -1936)

"BROTHER SQUARE-TOES"—REWARDS AND FAIRIES

If you can keep your head when all about you
Are losing theirs and blaming it on you,
If you can trust yourself when all men doubt you,
But make allowance for their doubting, too;
If you can wait and not be tired by waiting,
Or being lied about, don't deal in lies,
Or being hated, don't give way to hating,
And yet don't look too good, nor talk too wise:

If you can dream—and not make dreams your master;
If you can think—and not make thoughts your aim;
If you can meet with Triumph and Disaster
And treat those two imposters just the same;
If you can bear to hear the truth you've spoken
Twisted by knaves to make a trap for fools,
Or watch the things you gave your life to, broken,
And stoop and build 'em up with worn-out tools:

If you can make one heap of all your winnings
And risk it on one turn of pitch-and-toss,
And lose, and start again at your beginnings
And never breathe a word about your loss;
If you can force your heart and nerve and sinew
To serve your turn long after they are gone,
And so hold on when there is nothing in you
Except the Will which says to them: "Hold on!"

If you can talk with crowds and keep your virtue,
Or walk with Kings—nor lose the common touch,
If neither foes nor loving friends can hurt you,
If all men count with you, but none too much;
If you can fill the unforgiving minute
With sixty seconds' worth of distance run,
Yours is the Earth and everything that's in it,
And—which is more—you'll be a Man, my son!

PREFACE

And God said, "Behold, I have given you every herb-bearing seed which is upon the face of all the earth, and every tree in Which is the fruit of a tree yielding seed. To you it shall be for meat." *Genesis. 1:29*

"And the fruit thereof shall be *for* meat, and the leaf thereof for medicine." *Ezekiel 4712*

"He causeth the grass to grow for cattle, and herbs for the use of man." *Psalm 104:14*

"For one believeth he may eat all things; another who is weak eateth herbs." *Romans 14:2*

"And the leaves of the trees were for the healing of nations." *Revelation 22:2*

But powerful man-made organizations today tell us:

"What does God *know?* What does Buddha know? What does Hippocrates know? Eat aspirins, Bufferins, Valium, and after the side effects of these have caused worse problems, have chemotherapy. When your hair falls out, buy a Wig. I will give you prescriptions to deaden the pain, allow You to go through life like a Zombie, and when you are too sick for us to help you anymore, then go home and prepare to die.

But, if you should obtain help from an herbalist, nutritionist, or any other than a doctor of medicine, then we will persecute him if he makes you well, and persecute him if you should die like the doctor said you would.

If you live, then we will laugh at you and harass you, and tell you that you were never ill in the first place."

I believe that if Jesus were to suddenly appear in America today to heal people, He would be arrested for practicing medicine without a license. Telling people that they can be healed by proper eating, thinking and living would result in an immediate jail sentence.

They would not make Him walk the streets this time carrying a cross, but would rather crucify Him in all the establishment newspapers and other media. They would harass and ridicule Him, and they would drive Him out of the country.

For Jesus to help us in America today, He would have to live in the safety of Mexico, where all who wish to help people the natural way are forced to go.

Jason Winters

CHAPTER 1
TERMINAL CANCER

I walked into the Cobalt Radiation Department for the first time and was filled with despair. This department took care of patients suffering from head and neck cancer. There were about 20 patients in the waiting room, and I took my place among them. My heart was thumping, and with good reason, for the faces all around me showed fear and depression. I could smell death in the air. Most of the people had hardly any hair left due to the chemotherapy treatment. Ashtrays were scattered around the room and nearly everyone was smoking heavily When I mentioned that smoking is bad for your health, one patient said, "Well, it's too late for us now anyway, isn't it?"

One by one patients had their names called and would disappear behind a large lead door. When they came out they looked worse than before—and left hurriedly. I was worried as I had no idea what was behind that door. Would I too, soon have no hair and that look of terror in my eyes? I heard the nurse call my name and, as if in a daze, found myself following her into the treatment room

I had first noticed the swelling on the side of my neck when taking a steam bath at the Y.M.C.A. Although 46 years old, I was in top physical condition—running and swimming each day. Life was a ball for me, for I had a great wife, five nice kids and a good income. I smoked 30 cigarettes a day, and did some real hard drinking at least once a week. Rye whiskey was my favorite.

The lump seemed to ache deep inside my throat but I was not worried. I bought some lozenges and tried to forget about it. As the days went by the lump got bigger and bigger, but I avoided my doctor like the plague. I was unconsciously scared of what the lump might be. After a few more weeks even my friends noticed the swelling and remarked on it. I realized that I could not avoid the issue indefinitely, so I made an appointment with our family doctor.

He at once sent me to a surgeon. It resulted in dozens of x-rays, examinations at the Nuclear Medicine Center, scans, pills—and fear. At last it was decided that I must go into the hospital to have a small biopsy operation. The surgeon said it would take only half an hour and result in a scar a couple of inches long.

Soon after I checked into the hospital, a dear old lady came around with lots of strong, black coffee, white sugar and cream buns. She was trying hard to serve humanity, and no one ever told her she was serving what I later found out to be the very worst things a cancer patient, or anyone else for that matter, can eat and drink.

When I awoke from the operation I found that it had taken six and a half hours, and left a scar nine inches long. I saw immediately that my wife had been crying. I guess that was when I first knew for sure my condition was serious. The doctor walked in and said, "Terminal cancer. Infiltrating squamous cell carcinoma." The tumor was wrapped around my carotid artery and, to make matters even worse, was attached to the wall of my jugular vein.

After telling me three times that my condition was terminal, the doctor left me to my misery. My wife Jan went home to break the news to our five children. Thoughts of death crowded in on me from all sides. Reading, television, radio were all drowned out by the thoughts that soon I would be gone.

The next morning, when my doctor made his rounds, he did not find me in bed. Another patient and I were having an hilarious pillow fight from our wheelchairs. The doctor was furious.

"Don't you know you have terminal cancer? Don't you realize you should be in bed?" Because I was sure that all doctors are gods, I obeyed him quickly. But it was not long before I was out of bed again—this time to trudge around the hospital.

I walked around the whole place five times for exercise, and when I returned it was the head nurse's turn to be furious. She said the doctor had been complaining to her about me, and once again assured me that I had terminal cancer, and must at least stay in my room. It seemed to me that everyone was worried in case I forgot to die. The doctor even went so far as to lecture my wife on my behavior. "Doesn't he know he's got terminal cancer? Doesn't he believe me?"

Many tests followed and finally it was agreed what my treatment should be. I would have five weeks of cobalt radiation on my neck and head and then, if the swelling was down, I could have radical neck surgery. That meant the removal of my tongue, jaw bone, neck muscles and also the inside of my throat. To begin with I would receive three cobalt treatments each day for five weeks.

I felt better as soon as I left the hospital and walked down the street. I felt free, even though I got a lot of stares from people gaping at the bandages around my face and neck. At least they couldn't see the tumor.

My first appointment with the cancer clinic did not bother me too much. I had to be fitted for a plastic mask This went right over my head like the Count of Monte Cristo mask. There were three holes in one side for it to be attached to the cobalt machine, so that I could not move my head while being bombarded with radiation. I had to go back in one week for another fitting, and this really depressed me. I got so bad that I would not let my wife tell anyone that I had cancer. I could not stand the look of fear in their faces and the way even old friends changed toward me. I would not even let my children say the word cancer. That shows bow bad I had become.

The nurse in the cobalt room called my name—and it began. For five weeks I was to see my fellow patients gradually get weaker and weaker-then I would see them no more. One friend was a big, strong man who had a tumor on the side of his head. After many cobalt treatments his right eye started running, so they sewed it closed. I will always remember the terror in one good eye, as he looked at me in desperation. I said, "Don't worry, we will both get better," not believing it myself of course. My friend beamed and he shouted to all the other patients, "Did you hear that? Jason says we are both going to get better." It was many months later that I understood what he meant and why he was so happy. Since discovering he had cancer, he had been told repeatedly, "Terminal, terminal." I was the first one in the whole wide world to tell him he would get better, or to offer even any hope at all. He died two days later. I started taking 10 Valium tablets each day, so that I would not break down and cry, as well as six pain pills and six sleeping pills.

The cobalt treatment took away my taste, made it impossible for me to make saliva, burned the right side of my face and made my hair on that side fall out. Life was hell.

I went from 263 lbs. down to 170 lbs. My knees were shaky and I could not stay awake for longer than four hours at a time. It was then that I discovered the value of pure honey and vitamin E. As I would sit on the couch in shock, after the cobalt treatment, I would eat spoonfuls of honey. I could not taste it but I knew it was good for me. I stopped losing weight. I smeared the vitamin E on my burned face, and soon there was a great improvement. Doctors at the cancer clinic remarked how well I was taking the treatment. I told them what I was doing and they said that this was fine, but I was not to mention it to the others.

That remark puzzled me no end. I thought about it constantly. I did tell the others about it and they all started the same treatment with good results. But the doctors did not want me to tell anyone about it. The only answer I could figure out for this scared the heck out of me, but it probably saved my life. I started to realize that doctors are not gods after all. Maybe they can make mistakes too. If that was right, then maybe they had made a mistake about me. They all kept telling me to get my affairs in order and prepare to die, but perhaps I didn't have to die.

The next day the surgeon called me into his office. He

had decided to operate on me as soon as possible. Radical neck surgery. Removal of tongue, jaw bone and neck muscles. He went into great detail about the operation. When I asked him if I would live any longer from having the surgery, he said probably not. I looked him straight in the eye and said, "No." The doctor said, "What do you mean, No?" I said, "No operation." Then I stood up and walked out of his office. My heart was singing. I was going to keep my tongue and die in one piece.

Many times the doctor called my wife to tell her to get me into the hospital. Everyone was trying to get me there, even though everyone knew that I would die anyway. I couldn't understand it. I wondered who these people thought they were, asking me to have this terrible operation.

Then I heard about laetrile.

Laetrile

I heard that laetrile was made from apricot kernels and contained a little cyanide, necessary in our body in small amounts. I went at once to the health food store and bought six bottles of apricot kernels. I would eat about 50 a day. Soon the aching stopped and it looked as though the tumor was actually shrinking. I was elated and overjoyed. I did not worry about being cured. Just as long as I could keep it under control would be good enough for me.

When I ran out of the kernels I returned to the health food store for more. I was told that the government authorities had removed them from the shelves. I was horrified. How could anyone do this? The man in the health food store offered a possible explanation. If Laetrile could control cancer without all the operations and radiation that I had been through, what would happen to those people who work in cancer clinics by the thousands? They would be unemployed of course. Drug companies would lose millions, as would doctors, surgeons, anesthetists and nurses. Thirty major countries of the world were using laetrile in the treatment of cancer, but in North America it was banned.

Now, I had not yet gotten over the fact that doctors could make mistakes, so it took a lot of thought and investigation before I could realize the monstrous evil behind banning apricot kernels and laetrile. Dying people are sent home with the words, "We can't do anything for you," without the right to even try the biggest natural cancer fighter of all time.

I heard that the Contreras Clinic in Tijuana, Mexico, gave laetrile to patients, and my heart leapt. My wife and family made arrangements to accompany me, and off we went to Mexico.

We arrived at Centro Medico Del Mar in Tijuana early in the morning, and were soon surrounded by hundreds of Americans and Canadians all in the same position as myself. However, there was a difference from the other cancer clinics, for here I could see hope and enthusiasm shining on everyone's faces. After a complete examination by a doctor I was scheduled for laetrile injections each day and also put on a diet. I felt better already. For the first time in my life I started eating sensibly. Part of the cure must be a correct diet. Slowly I started building up my body. I thought of the old lady at the hospital with her coffee, white sugar and cream buns—all definite taboos at the clinic. Almost everyone here had a miraculous story to tell. I was slowly emerging from that long black tunnel of death, and I was ecstatic.

All of the patients here were terminal patients from the U.S. and Canada who had exhausted every avenue of orthodox treatment and were now trying this as a last resort. But miracles were happening here, and I thanked God that I had heard about it.

Each morning I would join in the line with hundreds of patients and when my turn came I would go into a cubicle and receive an enzyme enema. Right after this would come the laetrile injection. I can honestly say that there were no adverse effects experienced either by myself or any of the others. In 10 days the tumor had shrunk to half the size and the doctor stated that I could return home, but must take some laetrile tablets with me. I should take these three times each day. He said that my cancer was under control. I emerged from the clinic a happy man, hardly able to believe my good fortune.

When I arrived home I found that the cancer clinic had called many times. They wanted me to go up in front of a panel of doctors to be examined. They were all sure that I would have to have the operation. They knew nothing of my trip to Mexico.

I arrived early for the examination, anxious to see the expression on their faces when they discovered the tumor almost gone. One by one they examined me. But not one of them said a word to me. There were no smiles, no congratulations, no happiness at all. When I finally told them I had been taking laetrile, the doctor who had wanted to remove my tongue and so on, said that I could not have had cancer in the first place. Another said he must perform the operation anyway. I was horrified at the way these people acted, and left as soon as possible.

I thought the doctors would be overjoyed that my tumor had gone, would demand to know how I had done it, then hold press conferences around the world, stating just what happened. I thought of the thousands who were waiting for cobalt treatments, or were swallowing chemotherapy poison—so bad for the system it makes the patients' hair fall out, makes them vomit continually and fills the body full of toxins. I thought of the thousands who were waiting to enter the operating rooms of hospitals around the country, waiting to have colostomies and tumors removed. Terrible operations that removed the effects, but not the cause. I thought of all the thousands who that very week would be told they had cancer, and of how they would start dying immediately, because to them just the word cancer meant certain death. I felt like running through every cancer clinic in North America shouting that there is a control for cancer. Don't let that little old lady fill your ailing bodies with poisonous coffee and white sugar. Start eating God's health foods right now.

Nutrition

Now I know for sure that some readers are just as naive as I was about cancer, the medical profession, laetrile and all alternative therapies. I know that some people are so stubborn that they would rather die than admit they are wrong, and often do. If it's only your own life at stake, do as you wish, but if you are concerned with someone else's life, such as a loved one, a friend or relative, then remember, you are not God, and they deserve the benefit of the doubt. The whole reason for this book is to make you have a doubt, then maybe you will search for the truth.

"Things that are sweet in the mouth are bitter in the stomach." We know that too much sugar and sweet things are bad for us. And things that are bitter in the mouth may be sweet in the stomach. Bitter almonds and apricot kernels are very bitter and this is what laetrile is made from. God wants us to be healthy, so he gave us everything we need to live long, healthy lives. In this age of people proudly stating, "My son the doctor," I fear that we have made doctors our gods. It is interesting to note that in Oden's book, "**Thank God I Have Cancer**," it is shown that doctors and their families are among the unhealthiest in the nation. I quote:

10% already have cancer.
12% already have anemia.
21% have allergies.
24% have had major surgery.
30% are overweight.

These are the people who we run to with our sick bodies. These are the people we run to, instead of God. By the thousands we rush to psychiatrists, asking them to straighten out our minds. In reality, psychiatrists have the highest suicide rate of any group in the world. These are facts. Once in a while it is possible to find a doctor who works with nature and with God. This person will rely mainly on natural foods, vitamins and minerals to help your body regain health. When he performs surgery it is necessary. Find a doctor who believes God is greater than the medical associations, and you have found a jewel.

He will suggest you eat properly, he may well recommend B-17 (laetrile) because he will be unbiased and really care about you. He makes no money from laetrile, and there is not a drug salesman giving him free samples. This man cares so much because God is his boss-not a medical association. I feel that medical associations are like unions.' Designed to keep their members busy and financially secure. Can you name a nation other than America where a doctor expects to make hundreds of thousands of dollars each year? Can you name another country where doctors will not make house calls? Where they expect to retire at such an early age? Where they will charge you for not showing up for an appointment, but can keep you waiting for hours? Do they make money from sickness or health? Supposing that eating properly, along with God's natural immunity that He has given us all, kept everyone healthy, what would happen to the biggest business in America today?

It is interesting to note that in some provinces of China a doctor is paid by the government, a flat fee each month. When anyone gets sick, the doctor is fined a small amount. You see, he failed to keep his people healthy. He makes money out of health, whereas our doctors only can survive if we keep getting ill.

Find a God-loving, nutritionally-conscious doctor and you may avoid the treadmill of death. That is what I call orthodox cancer treatment. First the radiation which burns and scars, then the operation which removes the effect and not the cause, which also leaves you weak and in shock, and finally, if you have survived this, you are given chemotherapy. You are ill because your body is full of poisons, but now they are pouring more down your throat. Poison so drastic that sometimes they have to stop the treatment for a while so you can get stronger. Imagine a medicine so toxic that they have to take you off it so that you will get stronger by yourself. You have suffered all of this and yet God's system is still working within you. But oh, how it needs help. Nutrition—a change of mind about cancer. Yes, the treadmill of death. If you are an American, from the time you are told you have cancer until you die, you will have spent an average of $17,5OO. A doctor told me that once he or his associates discover cancer in a patient, they mentally write him off. He is as good as dead. I think doctors convey this attitude of helplessness to the patient.

Now I am a firm believer in mind over matter. So, if you have made a god of your doctor, then you will certainly do what he tells you, even to the extent of dying as expected. After all, faith can move mountains. Then why shouldn't you die when your medical god tells you that you should? It is hard to change from a negative to a positive attitude, especially when you have been bombarded with radiation, cut up with surgery and then poisoned with chemotherapy. But talk to the thousands of people at the laetrile clinics in Mexico and Germany. They all go to these clinics after the medical profession has given up on them. My telling you what is taking place there every day is not enough. You must take full responsibility for your own life. You must find Out this exciting truth for yourself.

Some people, of course, are so stubborn that they cannot be helped. Although it is heart- breaking there is nothing you can do. The following story is a typical example.

Two young boys, one ten years old and one seven, had identical tumors in the left leg. The seven-year-old's parents were well aware of nutritional cures. When told that major surgery was necessary, they refused, and the boy was put on a nutritional diet and laetrile. Six weeks later the tumor was gone and he has complete remission. His smiling face is a glorious sight to behold.

However, the 10-year-old's parents believed that if there was a cure for cancer, then the doctors would know about it. When they asked their doctor about laetrile he called it a useless toxic hoax, used by charlatans and quacks.

As of this writing, the little boy is waiting for his third operation. He has already lost his left leg. His hair has fallen out. My heart goes out to him and to the thousands of others on this medically-approved treadmill of death.

Can you imagine what would happen if suddenly the truth were to come out? As Red Buttons, the comedian, said to reporters of the "National Inquirer," 'People who suppress laetrile, and stop other people from using it are nothing more than murderers." Buttons' wife gained remission of cancer through laetrile.

Fred McMurray of TV fame gained remission of cancer through laetrile. A wonderful man who said "No" to orthodox methods and took that natural way back to health.

People involved in laetrile have been persecuted. Many have been taken to court, won the case, only to be taken to court again and again. This is harassment. Even though a person wins every case, he can go broke just defending himself. So the million dollar drug cartels win after all. The top doctor told me that as long as more people benefit from cancer than suffer from it, we will be happy to go along just like this. Hundreds of millions are spent on cancer research each year, providing many top-paying jobs. A startling fact to remember in all of this is that statistics indicate that one person in four will have cancer next year. No wonder, the way we are eating and drinking junk. No wonder our bodies are fighting a losing battle.

In spite of all the persecutions and harassments, those pushing for the right of patients to use laetrile are winning. We can now obtain laetrile (B17 or amygdalin) in most states and provinces, although it's not easy, and it is expensive. It is estimated that 3,000 people in Canada alone order laetrile every month. They have to order it from Germany or Mexico because the homemade stuff is not always pure. This average person spends about $100 each month on laetrile, which means that Over $300,000 each month is leaving a country with a population of just 20 million.

To get an idea of how much Americans are spending on

laetrile each month, just multiply that figure by 10. Laetrile is a God-given vitamin that attacks cancer cells and is completely non- toxic if obtained in its pure form.

Should the powers that be in North America make it difficult for the millions of people destined to get cancer in the next few years to obtain laetrile? The largest manufacturer of laetrile in Europe ships Out over 500,000 orders each month to doctors, hospitals, clinics and patients all over the world. Also, laetrile, in the form of bitter almonds and apricot kernels., has been in use to fight tumors for 4,000 years. Recently, while browsing through a book store in London, I was surprised to come across a book, first published in 1810 and written by Jacob Antworth. On page 81 be states that in order to eliminate growths, the kernels from apricots should be crushed and mixed with your morning oats' You will be glad to know that God did not put all His eggs in one basket, so to speak The following foods all contain laetrile'. Alfalfa, buckwheat, cassava, flaxseed, broad beans, lima beans, garlic, soya beans, berries, black-strap molasses, macadamia nuts, sprouts, rye, rice, bran, peas, Oats, millet and the seeds of apples, plums, cherries and, of course, apricots. So, start helping yourselves to God's way of killing cancer. Pancreatic enzymes are also very important to the cancer patient. Two tablets taken prior to laetrile allow the latter to work more effectively. It seems that the enzymes rush to the cancerous area where they Start eating away at the protein shell that usually surrounds and protects a tumor. This allows the laetrile to penetrate the tumor and release its cyanide Onto the cancer cells to kill them.

When you remember that all natural means were given~ us by God, it means that the authorities have rejected God's methods. I think that everyone knows that if you are for God, then you are spiritual, and if you are against God, then you are evil.

Americans told by their doctors to prepare to die are filling clinics in Mexico and Germany, and many are going home in a few weeks with their cancer in complete remission. These clinics are not run by quacks either. Most of the world's foremost cancer scientists believe that laetrile is a wonderful anticancer agent. Among them are Dr. N.R. Boujiane of Montreal, Dr. John Morrone, New Jersey; Dr. Hans Nieper, Germany; Dr. Contreras of Mexico and Dr. Navarro of Manilla. Of course, the findings of such men are discounted in America. They dare to take a different stand, and are often ridiculed. Jesus was persecuted for being different, and Giordano Bruno was burned at the stake for teaching that the world is round. Laetrile works in many, many cases and is certainly worth a try. It takes away the pain and makes one far more comfortable.

I have spoken to hundreds of people who should have died 20 years ago (according to their doctors), but they discovered laetrile, have taken it daily ever since and are as healthy as can be. I have gone into the laetrile story at great length because I am about to shock you, and before I do I want you to know that laetrile works for thousands of people.

My tumor started coming back. I was taking the enzymes and the 3,000 mgs. of laetrile every day, but the swelling started coming back. In shock, I increased the dosage but it did no good whatsoever.

After three weeks the tumor was as big as it was before, so I called the laetrile clinic. I was told that this sometimes, but rarely, happens, and there was not much that I could do. I was on a strict diet of fruit and vegetables with large doses of vitamins, but it was getting worse.

Now I really did live with death 24 hours each day It was as though I had been given life, only to have it snatched away. This time I really did prepare to die. I purchased all kinds of religious books and while my family went to work to keep groceries on the table, I read them all. In my misery I was struck by how many times herbs are mentioned in the Bible, even on the first page. Herbs as medicines showed up in so many different religions that it seemed to be too much of a coincidence. Hippocrates, father of medicine, stated that herbs shall be for medicine. So did Buddha and Krishna. Then I found that the North American Indians believed in herbs and used them as medicine; also the gypsies of Europe, and the Hunzas, and the Aborigines. All spiritual writings somewhere or other mention herbs for healing.

In desperation my mind cast about for decisions on what I should do. It would be so easy to do nothing, and to waste away. I was full of dread and fatigue, but I could not die yet. Besides, I was too scared to die. I must find the herbs that God put here for this purpose. And so started a search that took me around the world.

Healing Herbs

Once I started learning about herbs as medicine I did become a little excited, but not much, especially after my letdown with laetrile. The most powerful ancient herb for tumors was known to come from Asia. I went to every herbalist in my area, then telephoned others across the country. They had never heard of it except in old books from Asia. The more difficult this herb became for me to find, the more determined I was that I had to have it.

When I learned that it was available in Singapore, I started thinking about traveling there. The only problem was money. We had $6,OOO to our name, did not own a house or anything else worthwhile that I could get a loan on. Also, we had five kids to support. But still, we all felt that this was a matter of life and death. My eldest child went to stay with friends, and my 16 and 15-year-old sons quit school (we hoped, temporarily) and got lobs. I had many credit cards left over from my more affluent days and I figured I would use these to pay travel expenses. If I survived then I would pay them back, and if not, my wife would have to declare bankruptcy. So it came about that with our two youngest children, my wife and I boarded a plane—destination Singapore. The fact that my two children had to support me, one under each arm, caused the Singapore immigration some concern. For a moment it was touch-and-go on whether they would let me into the country We explained that I was merely airsick, which I am sure they did not believe, as the tumor was obvious to all. They decided in our favor and we soon found ourselves at the hotel. My wife lost no time in looking for the herb, which was not available in the stores in Singapore. At last she came upon an old lady living a distance from town, who cultivated the herb. Evidently she dug up the roots and boiled 50 lbs. in a large container. After boiling vigorously for 26 hours, she was left with a liquid concentrate which she sold for a very high price. Usually sold in half-ounce bottles, she was surprised when we asked for one pint. I was told that it would definitely get rid of my cancer. I can remember that I held that bottle with great reverence; after all, this is the very thing that the great Buddha suggested for tumors. I could hardly wait to get back to the hotel to start drinking it. The directions were to take one- eighth of a teaspoonful in a large glass of water, once each day, until well.

For 10 days I took the medicine, and when nothing happened, I doubled the dose. The tumor, although not getting any bigger, Stayed the same size exactly. A hurried visit to the old lady brought merely a shrug. She had no idea why it had not worked. She said, "Well at least it's stopped growing," and that was it. My wife insisted that we buy another pint from her, even though we still had a lot left over. Jan was so impressed by the old lady's knowledge that she figured even if it did not cure cancer, it would prevent her getting it. Both her parents had died of the disease.

We left Singapore feeling very low indeed. I felt the herb did not work, and maybe that was why it didn't. We left for our next destination which was Tucson, Arizona.

Years before I had been a stunt man and a bit actor in Hollywood. We had made a few films with Audie Murphy in a place called Old Tucson, just a few miles from Tucson. Old Tucson was built in the old western style for Hollywood. Many western movies were made there, including "Apache Agent," in which I played. I had learned at that time about a tea which most Indians, especially Mexican Indians, drank for health, and that's what prompted our visit. In Arizona we soon located the herb, known as chaparral, or the creosote bush (divaricata). Once again we heard that this remedy had been passed down through the ages and would prevent or get rid of cancer.

We stayed at the Santa Rita Hotel in Tucson then moved to a small motel with a kitchen. The chaparral tea which I had to make five times each day was putrid, and smelled as bad as it tasted. It was enough to make a healthy man sick, but I persisted. It seemed to do nothing at all, except make me sick, but looking back now I feel that although I was not getting better, I was not getting worse. But at the time, so obsessed with death and dying, I was too depressed to notice.

In Tucson, a nutritionist who learned of my condition, told us that in Europe there were many old remedies for different ills, even cancer. He said that because there is socialized medicine there (free doctors and hospitals), doctors don't expect to become rich overnight. Because of this they are more open to alternative, inexpensive therapies. He said that if ever he became ill he would return to England for that reason alone. And so, as a last resort, we decided to visit England.

With five pounds of chaparral and a pint and a half of the Singapore potion, we boarded the plane for London. We had already spent most of our cash and were now on credit cards. That was the only time in my life that I have ever appreciated credit.

Now, I have dozens of relatives in England, but I would not let my wife contact any of them. I did not want them to see me like this, and I wanted no tears. This is the part of the trip that I enjoyed, because this was the country I was born in, and it did me good to see the beautiful countryside once more. In my heart I knew that the visit was not really necessary, but just returning home meant defeat, and going to England postponed the inevitable for a while.

I called the Archbishop of Canterbury and asked him what herb he thought it was that was referred to so many times in the Bible to purify a person's blood. After consulting his staff he informed me that it was "red clover."

I chopped up clover blossoms to make a very nice tea, which I also started drinking—at the rate of five glasses each day. This meant that I was busy making tea all day, first with the Asian herb, then chaparral, then red clover.

On the fourth day I became very ill indeed. My legs were shaking and I felt terribly sick. I had to stay in bed. I stopped taking all the herbs and readied myself for death. Two days later I felt a little better and my wife Jan wanted to return home to Canada. This whole adventure had been very rough on her; she looked worn out, and wanted to return to whatever little security she had left. When we arrived our credit cards were promptly confiscated and we found we owed many thousands of dollars. Bill collectors were calling on the telephone and knocking on the door constantly; we were all very worried. My youngest son, Robin, was sent home from school because he broke down and started crying. When asked why, he said, "My dad is dying of cancer."

As a last resort, I started back on the herbal teas again. One morning, I can remember it well, I was at my lowest ebb. I thought to heck with it, I'll mix all the herbs together.

The Mixture

I was sick and tired of washing the tea pot all the time prior to making another type of herbal tea. It was five minutes to ten on a Wednesday morning. I made the tea combination and a miracle happened.

I could feel it with that first swallow. It seemed to ring a distant bell, a long past memory. It screamed at me that this was what I needed. Strength seemed to pour through my body. That day I made a gallon of the tea and drank it all. When my family walked through the door they could see the difference in my face. I was enthusiastic, excited and overjoyed. Tears filled all of our eyes. We did not understand what had happened but we all knew that something wonderful had taken place. Day after day I drank one gallon regularly. Strength and vitality returned, but mostly it was my frame of mind. I was going to live, I knew it. All depression left me, all morbid thoughts. The more excited I became, the smaller the tumor got; the smaller the tumor became, the more I got excited. Within three weeks the tumor had gone completely. Everyone called it a miracle, because in nine weeks I returned to work. I was not as healthy as before—I was healthier, and God, how I enjoyed every minute of life.

My case became well known throughout the whole area and people with terminal cancer started lining up outside the door, just to talk to me. They all wanted the tea. Then my local priest called me into his office and said, "Look Jason, I know and so do you, that you have found something for cancer, and for other illnesses too. Why my hemorrhoids that I have suffered with for 20 years disappeared in two weeks of drinking your tea. Many other things are happening to people drinking it too. Good things. You have something here, and if you do nothing about it you can be guilty of the sin of omission. But, if you do decide to do something about it you can expect to be persecuted severely. The officials in North America won't let you ruin a multi-million-dollar-a-year business without a fight, and they have the money and the power to ridicule you and to threaten you"

After much thought I decided to tell my story to the world. A small newspaper took up the story first, which resulted in over 300 telephone calls and 1,000 letters, plus a big lineup outside the door, from 8 a.m. until past midnight. My boss fired me because I was supposed to sell refrigerators, but cancer patients filled the store and we could not move. Everyone wanted the tea. Separately the herbs would not work for me; together they were a miracle. I started importing the ingredients and mixing them in four-ounce bags, which I would give to anyone who wanted some. They, in exchange, would give a donation so that I could get more herbs.

The radio station told my story, which increased the customers tenfold. Never in the history of the radio Station had they received so many calls as they did about that particular program.

One man with a brain tumor received such help that the doctors pronounced him well. Without my permission he had advertising made up about my tea. He wanted the world to know about it—he wanted to help everyone. He got me into trouble and my first persecutions began.

People started flying in to see me from Australia, Germany, and many other places in the world, and I was flooded under. The police became regular visitors to my place, making sure that I did not tell anyone that the herbs were any good for anything. But I didn't need to say anything. The world was so desperate for something natural that would work that I was constantly running out of herbs.

I started receiving many offers from people and companies, one even from a priest. I had never met this man before, but he came up to me and said, "Take me in as your partner and we will make a million. We can charge $50 a four-ounce bag and I can get the hell out of this church." All this, in front of a witness! I found it hard to believe, and told him a definite "No."

Now the priest had in his congregation a particularly violent man who needed help desperately. The priest, mad at me for not accepting his offer, set this man on me. He actually attacked me once in the church. The priest would incite the man, whom I will call Mr. H. Strangely enough, one of the first letters reporting a cure was from Mr. H.'s wife. So furious were the priest and Mr. H. that they still, to this day, type letters to magazines and newspapers, and sometimes even to dying people saying, "Mr. Winters never had cancer, and if you want more information call Reverend...," and of course the letters are unsigned. So persecution and hatred come from various places. When a national magazine ran a 28-page story on my experiences and the tea, I thought it would be easy, but they took three months to put it together, and interviewed hundreds of people involved.

As far as the editors are concerned the tea works, and

now they are steady drinkers of it themselves. At the time the article was being prepared, the Canadian version of the F.D.A. showed up and went through our files, taking the names of all of our customers and confiscating all the tea we had. By this time I had 3,000 people relying on me for the tea. They took up a collection and I left for Nassau in the Bahamas where I set up a company.

When an article came out in a magazine, we started receiving over 2,000 orders each day, and that has continued with absolutely no advertising whatsoever. We had to hire all the unemployed people we could get to help us, and still the business grew. Over 1,000 letters each month pour telling of the relief and cures obtained from all kinds of ills. Hollywood stars, politicians, all types of medical men, attorneys, truck drivers, etc., order regularly.

Greed caused people to do some pretty terrible things. The priest previously mentioned, for instance, knowing that I had left the country, gathered a group of people around him and they are now selling an herbal mix, using my name, knowing that it is nowhere near the same tea. A health food distributor in Canada also could see the money in this, and is putting out a phony tea under my name. These people are, of course, trading lives for dollars, and I mention this so that the reader knows enough to be careful.

I have recently turned over the formula and distributorship in the United States to Tri-Sun North America. The hatred, bitterness, greed and harassment proved too much for me to handle. Besides this, my values have changed. Money is not as important to me as being alive. I feel wonderful about life, and about God, who cured me. Greed and bitterness cause stress, and I think that stress causes cancer, so I will leave all those feelings behind.

Why The Formula Works

God placed a certain herb in each continent to cure illness by simply purifying the blood. Life is in the blood, and if anything purifies the blood then a person's God-given natural immunity will have a chance to take over and fight all disease.

It is as simple as that.

The herb God put in Asia will not grow elsewhere, and the same goes for chaparral of North America and red clover of Europe. If you try to grow these herbs elsewhere they do not thrive because of soil deficiencies.

Jesus spoke of one herb for purifying the blood, Buddha of another herb in Asia, and the Native American spirit fathers of yet another.

Now in those days; before coffee, white sugar, processed foods and fast food outlets, any one of these herbs would have done the trick on its own.

However, we who live today have such toxic bodies that we don't know what good health really is; after all we have nothing to judge it by. We are fed on canned milk from birth, then doctored up cow's milk, canned baby food, graduating to hamburgers, french fries, coffee and white sugar. That is why just one of these herbs would not work on me. I was so full of toxins, as you are, that it took the combined efforts of the three most powerful herbs to bring me back to health.

I did not know it at the time but while I was drinking the tea at first I became sick to my stomach. I should have noticed this as a good sign. All that was happening was that the herbs were clearing my body of poison, and it was taking place so fast that it was overpowering my liver. A good sign. What a person should do in that case is take it easy for three days, then start on the herbs again. Eventually the body will be purified and you will not feel sick any more.

On a recent trip to England I was met with open arms by the medical profession. They were anxious to try my tea. One radionics practitioner tested the tea with his machine and found that it raised his energy level from 47 to 88. This may not mean much to the average reader, but to anyone in the know about radionics it is quite astounding. Even the British royal family has its own herbalist, a Mrs. Blackie, who has treated the Queen and her family for years.

Dr. Pierce—Top Oncologist

Word got out to the media and I started getting many calls. Dr. Pierce, an oncologist, came to me and said that the had studied my case and could he have a sample of the ingredients so that he could test them in his laboratory. Of course I gave him as much as he needed and he left. Two weeks later he called me on the phone to say, "Jason, those herbs didn't cure your illness. All they did was to purify your blood to such an extent that your body's immune system healed you." He continued, "We found something strange, however. You know that red clover and sage are acknowledged around the world as blood purifiers. Well, when you mixed them with herbalene that Buddha spoke about, the herbalene acted as a catalyst and made the other two twenty-seven times stronger. You see, Jason, God did not just throw us down here and say, 'there's ten thousand fast food restaurants, pollution in the air and poison in the water, have fun!"

"No, he gave us an immune system to take care of our bodies, it is natural to be healthy, unnatural to be unhealthy. In biblical days, any one of those herbs you used could and did purify a person's blood on its own. But today our blood is so toxic that it took the combined efforts of the three herbs to purify your blood and let your body heal itself," he concluded.

I was impressed. Here was a top oncologist taking his time to explain all this to me.

Upon our arrival back in Nassau we found thousands of complaints from people who had not received their tea, ordered weeks before. We checked back and found that all had been sent via the Post Office within two days of receiving the order. It seemed as though the powers that be had finally found a way to stop us from helping people. During a period of three months over 10,000 packets of tea disappeared in the post, and we have never found them. The customers, knowing nothing of our problems, started to write some pretty awful letters to us, some even blaming us for their spouse's death.

This of course bothered me to no end, so we kept sending out second orders free, by the thousands. In spite of all our troubles, the letters kept coming in telling of cures for cancer, arthritis, varicose veins, hemorrhoids, skin problems and much more. Now that the herbs are supplied by one company, these problems have been solved.

Along with complaints come pitiful, sad stories—some that have made us weep. One lady sent back the tea, saying, "My doctor says I have only a month or so to live and he doesn't want me using this stuff." And another, "My husband sneaks your tea into the hospital every night in a thermos. The doctor would be furious if he knew what it was, but we told him it's brandy. He feels better each day and the doctor thinks it's his doing." But the saddest case of all is the following: A woman of 35 came to me because she had cancer of the breast. I spoke to her about my case and she became a different person, excited and happy. She visited her doctor that afternoon and he told her that the cancer had spread to her right eye and brain. She said "What can I do doctor, shall I take herbs, laetrile, shall I pray?" His answer was, "Don't waste your time on all that stuff, it's all garbage. Just face it and get your affairs in order." The lady went home and killed herself that same day.

Please listen to me when I say that "**cancer does not mean death**." We usually start dying as soon as we hear that word. We have been brainwashed into thinking it's a killing disease and we are supposed to die from it. The doctor may well insist that you believe him when he tells you how much time you have left. No one knows how long you have got—it's largely up to you. If you believe the doctor, then you will die right on time. We have seen this on many occasions. Your life is up to you, so don't believe any doctor who condemns you to die just because he doesn't understand your illness. There are thousands of people I have met who were expected to die of cancer years ago. They all had one thing in common, they were smarter than their doctors. My doctor is so upset that he was wrong about me, that I didn't die as he said I should, that he won't even talk to me now. Believe me, dear fellow sufferer, if there is one person I do not wish ever to talk to again, it's him.

All I am asking you to do is to change your mind about things, and live. God gave you life, and it's up to you to keep it. Eat properly, think properly, and you will soon notice a difference.

An experiment recently in Europe was very interesting. People with cancer were gathered together, and were all asked this question, "What do you think your cancer looks like, and what do you think of the medicine that you are given to fight it?"

Group A were in accord that their cancer was like a big black rat, very strong and devouring everything, even the medicine.

Group B said that their cancer was a small lump surrounded by white cells (natural immunity), that were gradually eating the cancer away.

Although these people had the same cancer in the same degree, group A died and group B lived. Please think about this. Jesus said that faith can move mountains.

Dr. Fernie has another theory on cancer. He claims that cancer patients all fall into a certain category. He explained it to me this way: A woman of 45 has a husband who now devotes all his time to his business. Her children have left home either to get married or to live elsewhere. She develops breast cancer. Suddenly she is at the top of her husband's list so far as attention goes, and the children come rushing home. Could we get cancer just to get our own way? I know that if we concentrate we can eliminate pain, or make ourselves happy or sad. If Dr. Fernie is right and we unconsciously make ourselves ill, then we can just as easily make ourselves well. Faith can move mountains!

At another clinic only a cancer patient who has passed a

test as a positive thinker will be accepted. Also, the only visitors allowed in to see the patients are positive thinkers—ones who will spread hope and life and enthusiasm. It seems to work too.

A clinic in England treats its cancer patients with a steady diet of asparagus tips. This seems to work. Yet another gets good results with massive doses of vitamins A and C, plus six glasses of carrot juice each day.

Another believes that we get cancer because our pancreas is not putting out enough enzymes to eat up the protein in our diet, so they prescribe 30 pancreatic enzymes each day.

One doctor of nutrition has had success fighting cancer with a solution made from poison ivy. One man cured cancer, he assures me, with two teaspoons of gasoline each day.

Another man with lung cancer refused to go into the hospital for the treadmill of death. He said he would not accept that he had cancer, and it went away. Many say that my tea brings such hope to people who have had all hope taken away, that they believe they will get well as quickly as I—so they do. Faith can move mountains. As soon as we find out that the medical profession isn't the answer, and people are living in spite of phoney death sentences, then we have to choose between many therapies. It seems that everyone who has beaten terminal cancer writes a book about it, and claims to know the secret and the true answer. I am not one of these. I say that seeing that it's your life you are going to save, then take the best from all of them. None of the things they recommend will hurt you, but leave out the gasoline please, there is an oil shortage.

Let's look at it this way. If there are many types of cancers then there could be many types of cures. You must, of course, purify your blood first. Now then, we are about to take advantage of all the knowledge gained by people who fought for their lives and won. Please remember that most of them were in worse shape than you to begin with. First thing, when that nice little old lady shows up with the coffee, tell her to disappear and take the coffee with her. Don't let her forget the white sugar and cream because you won't be needing those either. Now, if you are in a hospital it may be a little tough because everyone knows it is almost impossible to get well in a hospital. Just be careful of what you eat. Try to get lots of fresh fruit and vegetables, raw if possible. Whole wheat bread only. Eat 20 raw almonds each day. Take five pancreatic enzymes before each meal. Don't eat canned foods, and stay away from salt. Eat 12 ounces of asparagus each day, and if it must be canned, use the Jolly Green Giant kind because it has less acid in it. Try to get lots of fresh carrot juice and drink it within an hour of being made. Try to get some laetrile tablets and take four 500 mg. tablets each day.

Now, I don't want to shock you, but coffee is good for one thing, and one thing only. That is a coffee enema. You laugh, but thousands of ex-cancer patients do this daily and it's simply wonderful for ridding the body of toxins and cleaning the liver. Three cups of strong black coffee in an enema bag, luke warm. Lie on your right side and try to hold it for 15 minutes, then expel. You will soon find out how much you needed it. You will find it hard to believe all the junk you have been hanging on to all these years. Please don't worry about this becoming habit forming. I know of many people who have had coffee enemas every day for years. As soon as they stop they eliminate naturally again. At one clinic in France they won't let you stay if you refuse to have your regular coffee enemas. Here you are already worrying if it's habit forming when, just now, you were sure you were going to die right away. You see, we've made progress already.

You can drink as much of the herbal tea as you wish. It's God's natural food so it won't harm you and there are no side effects. Even the Russian hockey team drinks it daily, just to stay healthy.

One more thing. If you are going to keep on smoking, then forget about all of the above. Out of the thousands of terminal patients that I have spoken to during the last three years, not one smoker has survived, and it didn't matter what he tried. Once a heavy smoker myself, I can hardly stand to be in the same room with someone who is smoking.

You must quit smoking if you want to live, and if you want to live then you will. Faith can move mountains.

Radiation Poisoning—Healing The Side Effects

If you have been subjected to cobalt radiation and/or x-rays then you are suffering a little from radiation poisoning. It's no accident that doctors and nurses disappear behind lead doors while~ they bombard you with rays.

How to get rid of the ill effects of radiation poisoning.

Pour one pound of pure salt purchased from a health food store (not iodized), and one pound of baking soda, into a hot bath and stay in the water for 20 minutes. Immerse the part affected if possible. Do this twice each week for one month. If you have any surgical scars or radiation burns, spread vitamin E liberally over the affected parts.

A New Life

In closing I would like to say that my heart goes out to you. I don't know you but I know what you are going through. Thousands are going through the exact same thing as you right now—you are not alone. You have been luckier than the others though, for you found this book, and now you know that you don't have to die; you can live on in health as so many of us are doing. You can tell of your recovery and so help others. I didn't start to live until I had cancer, and I know that it will be the same for you. Miracles are happening every day in many places. At the Hans Nieper clinic in Germany, the Contreras clinic in Mexico, Dr. Kelly in Washington. Just go and see for yourself. You will be surprised. Read the many books at your local health food store, all about cancer. Cancer is a mystery only to the medical profession who knows nothing whatsoever about the most important thing in the world, nutrition. Stay away from negative people—you don't need their bad vibrations. Tell them to stay away until you are better. Start planning on how you will be spending next year and the year after. Plan to spread the good word throughout the country. Cancer no longer means death.

Modern day medicine in North America spends all of its time treating effects instead of causes. They never find out what causes a swelling, but they treat the swelling. If you cut your finger badly, and then let it get dirty, blood poisoning will set in. Soon a red line will travel up your arm and cause a lump under your armpit. The correct way to treat this is to get rid of the poison and also treat the finger, then the lump will disappear.

Right now it's up to you, completely. Think that you are going to live—like Jason Winters and thousands of others. Watch what you eat. Remember that out of seven years of medical training American doctors have only had six hours on nutrition. You are solely, completely and definitely 100 percent responsible for yourself. Whatever other people want to do to you, you must always remain captain of your ship.

If you are a cancer patient, I know what you are going through. In the hospital you are surrounded by people who think you are going to die because they don't understand cancer. Red-eyed friends and relatives gather around your bed telling you that everything is going to be fine, even though they don't believe it.

You are there with cancer and your mind runs wild. Every little ache and pain says, "My God it has spread to my right eye, my left shoulder, my big toe." Just because you have cancer does not mean that you are immune from all of the everyday aches and pains that everyone has to endure. Ninety-nine times out of 100 the pain you feel is totally unrelated to cancer. Get that firmly set in your mind. The white cells are eating your cancer, and with a little help from you the tumor may soon be gone.

For you, getting well again will include purifying your body by freeing it of toxins. Fruits, vegetables, fresh juice and the herbal tea will do this, as long as you are not pouring more poison into your body at the same time.

You also need an enema regularly. It comes as a great surprise to many people to learn that Jesus spoke to the Essenes about enemas. As a matter of fact, there is a whole sermon that He gave on the subject of healing in **"The Gospel of Peace**."

"Seek therefore a large trailing gourd, having a stalk the length of a man; take out its innards and fill it with water from the river which the sun has warmed. Hang it upon the branch of a tree, and kneel upon the ground before the angel of water, and suffer the end of the stalk of the trailing gourd to enter your hinder parts, that the water may flow through all your bowels. Afterwards rest kneeling on the ground before the angel of water and pray to the living God that he will forgive you all your past sins, and pray to the angel of water that he will free your body from every uncleanness and disease. Then let the water run out from your body, that it may carry away from within it all the unclean and evil-smelling things of Satan...And this holy baptizing by the angel of water is: Rebirth unto the new life."

Pick up this book and its sequel, "The Gospel of the Essenes," and read them carefully. They show that God really does want us all to be healthy-and that is why He gave us instructions that are so explicit. We must pay close attention to this wisdom, remembering that the internal parts of our bodies are perfect places for breeding all types of germs and bacteria, being dark, warm and damp.

Take a positive step; don't think about it, just do it. Buy a bag of fresh fruit. An apple, an orange, a banana and a packet of unblanched almonds or apricot kernels. Go for a walk and as you walk eat the fruit and know that with every bite you are getting enzymes enough to help you. Each step you take will build up your muscles, and the apricot kernels or almonds will give you protein and B17. Already you are doing something sensible to get back to good health. Do this twice a day. You will soon be over the shock and in a better frame of mind. Know with every step you take that another reader in the next town is doing the same thing. We have reports that thousands are doing just this, every day, across the country. Now is the time to get into step with this new army of people. They and you are following others who have already won the fight.

Please believe me when I say that this could be the most important turning point of your life. You have at last stopped your headlong, selfish rush through life, and now you can stand still for a moment, and look around. Those of you who have not noticed the beauty of the world will certainly do so now. Those who were their own god, ignoring their Father in heaven, will find themselves forced to follow God's wisdom in order to survive, and will love Him for every day He gives them. Be humble, assure Him that you will help others from now on, and if you mean it you can live a very long, happy life. Today is the day you start living. God will bless you.

Chapter 2

The Immune System

The world's leading manufacturer of laetrile (amygdalin), with head offices in Germany, explains cancer this way:

"In spite of numerous costly efforts of medical science, the reason for the uncontrolled division of cancer cells is still unknown, Even a single cell shows a remarkable ability to adapt and survive.

If its environment is disturbed or changed, the cell will immediately adapt itself.

This powerful adaptability is comparable to the growing tolerance of insects to pesticides. It is definitely a fact that inflammation or constant stress can lead to cancer. The formation of a cancerous tumor is the defense of the attacked cell to survive.

The immune system in our body detects and controls the beginning of inflammation. It gives the order to remove or neutralize damaged or destroyed cells.

But if stress or inflammation continue, for example, in skin cancer by overexposure to the sun, or in the cancer of the stomach and intestines by permanent psychological stress, enzymes give orders for cell division in order to bring the body back to its original healthy state.

The natural survival process begins. But the sick cells confuse the immune system by posing as healthy ones. The result is the gradual reduction of constant orders for cell destruction.

This weakened immune system can no longer differentiate between a masked, resistant cancer cell and a healthy one. Therefore an uncontrolled division of sick cells takes place.

The immune system of the cancer patient must be activated to the point where it can once again identify the sick, steadily dividing cancer cells, and kill them. This means that the immune system must be forced into an emergency situation. Many practitioners have been successful by administering mega doses of certain vitamins, vegetables or mineral substances. This brings about an elevation of the immune system where it can once again identify and destroy cancer cells. Unfortunately, unwanted side-effects can occur through such overdoses.

Amygdalin/laetrile/B17 is an extract from bitter almonds or apricot kernels. It is of the utmost importance that only the purest form of this substance is used.

The atomic construction of this substance consists of a cyano group which is very toxic. Only the right, exact procedures in its making will guarantee the ineffectiveness of these toxic substances. Now harmless, the cyan in the laetrile simulates an alarm situation in the cancerous body. Our bodies not only need vitamins and minerals, but also enzymes. It is therefore of the utmost importance that enough enzymes are administered directly to the bloodstream during the phase of activation.

Many alternative therapy clinics are administering an intravenous drip solution of enzymes and laetrile at the same time. This is most successful. Clinical tests have shown almost instant relief even to long-suffering cancer victims.

Also an insulin-dependent diabetic, for instance, once the pancreas was activated in this manner, showed such progress that insulin injections could be drastically reduced. Rheumatic and gouty pains disappeared."

This information was sent to me for entry in this book. I have visions of bleary-eyed cancer patients asking, "What did all that mean?" It means simply this:

If your God-given immune system was working properly, you would not have cancer. We now have to start it working. Laetrile will set off an alarm that will wake up your immune system.

Early Warning Signs of Cancer

After talking to over 10,000 cancer victims we found that in every case they had suffered at least three, and often all, of the following danger signals from three to eighteen months prior to cancer. There are other warnings which the body may provide, so if in doubt seek medical advice.

1. Weakening of the eyes, necessitating two or three changes of eye glasses in just a few months.
2. Fatigue. You can never get enough rest. You are as tired when you get up in the morning as when you retired at night. You have little or no energy.
3. Nerves. You become easily agitated and quickly fly into a rage. You hurt the ones you love self pity overcomes you and you could easily cry. You become too nervous to go out alone or enter a crowded room.
4. Depression. Life no longer seems worth living. Nothing excites you any more. Morbid thoughts creep into your mind. You quite often become preoccupied with death.
5. A strange tingling, aching sensation deep in your bones. In bed you feel that you must keep changing positions, and when you do the aching only goes away for a few minutes.
6. Loss of interest in sexual intercourse.

Anxiety

A well-known psychiatrist said, "In the beginning was the word, and the word was anxiety." This pretty well sums up most people's lives. We worry about the endless varieties of hazards, difficulties and disappointments that lay ahead of us.

From the moment we are born, we are surrounded by uncertainties and insecurities. Murphy's Law tells us that life is tough, that few things work out well, and that if a thing can go wrong it usually will. We find out that our idols have feet of clay, that doctors can be wrong, that our favorite movie star is really quite terrible. We are told that God is dead, and there is no one left to fight the F.D.A. No one can stop them putting poisonous fluoride in our drinking water, or tons of white sugar in baby food. There is no one powerful enough to say "stop" to all the drug ads for high blood pressure, or Valium, aspirins and Bufferin.

You meet a top reverend (I did), who, in the quiet of his study, laughed at the virgin birth and called Billy Graham a charlatan.

Fear is something tangible, and we can usually deal with that. But anxiety is a very different matter. Anxiety is a state of mind, and is far more lethal. I say lethal because all of these problems eventually manifest themselves in physical illness.

People suffering from anxiety usually do not know which way to turn, so they do nothing. This only increases our anxiety This, of course, is a mistake.

Growing up is often one long anxiety. "How is my school work? What about the pimples on my face? What job should I choose? Will I be able to keep it? Will people like me?" Then, a few years later, we fall in love and get married. "Will it last? Will he still love me? Who will change first? Who will die first? Will I be able to cope?"

No wonder we keep getting ill. With anxiety a person has usually become inbound, an introvert. Serving others is a surefire way to become mentally well. Believing in God and keeping busy serving others with kindness and love will usually dispel all your anxieties.

Believing in God is the prime prerequisite because anyone who thinks their life has no meaning, that the world happened by accident, and there is no purpose to anything, has a damn good right to have anxieties. I would suggest that anyone who feels this way is well qualified for a job with the authorities.

Tests have shown that most cancer patients suffer from anxiety prior to the appearance of the tumor. My case was no exception. Months before my tumor, I felt nervous, tense and strangely agitated, even walking into a crowded room bothered me. My right tonsil (site of later cancer) would itch constantly. On going to a doctor, he put me on Valium. This depressed the symptoms and allowed the cancer to grow undetected, until it was almost too late.

Tests also show that most people suffering from mental disorders are simply allergic to certain foods or have a total lack of a necessary chemical or vitamin in their body.

NUTRITION AND HEALTH

Copied from the Surgeon General's report

Role of Vitamin A and Carotenoids in Cancer

A large body of evidence suggests that foods high in vitamin A and carotenoids are protective against a variety of epithelial cancers (Mettlin 1984; Kummet, Moon and Meyskens 1983; Bertram, Kolonel and Meyskens 1987; Palgi 1984)

Vitamin A in foods occurs in two forms: (1) preformed vitamin A (retinol and retinol esters) from animal foods and (2) provitamin A (Carotenoids that the body can convert to vitamin A) from plant foods. Hundreds of other carotenoid compounds in fruits and vegetables seem to have no vitamin A activity. Beta-carotene-containing foods have been extensively studied in cancer epidemiology (Peto et al, 1981). Although beta-carotene is most efficiently converted (Linder 1985), it still has only one-sixth the biologic activity of Retinol. Many reports on the effects of vitamin A do not specify whether they are studying preformed vitamin A, carotenoids in general, retinoid analogs of vitamin A, or beta-carotene along (NRC 1982). This chapter uses the term vitamin A to include all of the above unless otherwise specified.

Epidemiological studies have used food intake records to analyze the intake of beta-carotene, carotenoids, and retinol, or a "vitamin A index" that combines these. A methodological difficulty is that foods, such as green and orange-yellow vegetables may contain protective factors in addition to carotenoids (Mettlin 1984). Other complications are presented because inverse correlations between blood levels of beta-carotene and retinol and risk for cancer have been identified in some, but not all, studies (Willett and MacMahon 1994). Future studies that better distinguish the individual effects of beta-carotene, carotenoids, retinol, and other food components will require improved dietary assessment methods (Russell-Briefel, Caggiula, and Kuller 1985).

Chapter 3

Four Years Later...

Tibet

The ancient Yogi stepped out of his small hut, high in the Himalayas. In spite of the bitter cold weather and the deep snow, he was clad only in a thin loincloth. His bare feet sank deep into the snow as he made his way to the small field opposite his hut.

He then sat down in the snow, arranged himself in the lotus position, closed his eyes and began to concentrate. In his mind his spine was a white-hot flame, increasing in size and temperature.

The strangers that had gathered to watch were all, without exception, wearing very thick clothing, including heavy parkas with fur hoods. They were still cold.

The old man did not move a muscle, but soon it was evident that he was perspiring. Beads of sweat poured down his forehead, arms and chest.

Whispering started among the bystanders. "Could it be, is it possible?" Yes, it is true. The snow around the Yogi had started to melt and trickle away, only to refreeze once outside a six-foot radius.

Wider and wider became the circle around the man. The snow once four inches deep had now gone, and the bare earth could be seen.

Another 15 minutes found the Yogi in the center of a circle six feet in diameter and completely devoid of snow. Steam arose from this circle, and from the man.

The Yogi then stood up and returned to his hut.

The bystanders walked over to the circle and, taking off their gloves, felt the bare ground with their hands. The heat was like an oven. It soon cooled, however, and the bystanders continued on their way.

Only two were left standing in the circle. Jan looked up at me from under the hood of her parka, and I returned her gaze. No words were spoken as we turned and walked slowly down the mountain trail to the village of Nangchen Japo.

Learning that there is more to life than just existing, more to life than eating, drinking, breathing and working has brought to my life renewed enthusiasm and vitality.

To find myself standing on a mountain in Tibet, watching the ancient Yogi definitely was exciting, and a far cry from selling refrigerators back in Canada.

It came about this way: One morning, while relaxing in my study in the 16th Century cottage that we now call home, on the south coast of England, I received a very strange letter postmarked China.

It was from a Buddhist group which had been using the herbal tea for over a year. They were excited about it and invited me to visit with them as their guest. All I had to do was to get there.

Jan, my wife, was excited about this also, for to get a letter of praise from far-off China, a country wise in the use of herbs for thousands of years, was praise indeed.

Arriving at the temple tired, hot and out of breath, I was shown to a room with only a table, one chair and a slab of rock on which to sleep. On the table was a pitcher full of water and a bowl to wash in. A drone of male singers echoed through the myriads of rooms and hallways and into my room. As I washed a chill came over me suddenly as I remembered where I was, alone, thousands of miles away from home in an atmosphere so totally foreign to me.

Another very old man came into the room carrying a bowl of rice with some kind of vegetable mixed with it, and a bowl of brown drink. I tasted it carefully and behold, it was my herbal tea.

Going into the main hall later that day, I noticed that only men were to be seen, and that these men were all of great age. The eldest was by far the wisest, and although very short and thin, he looked as though he was amazingly healthy. His voice was high and melodic, and he spoke English in flowery tones. He greeted me and shivers ran down my back, and for some unknown reason, the hair on the back of my neck stood on end.

"Did you know, Mr. Jason, that you are 49 years younger than the youngest man at this temple? You are now 51 years of age, are you not?" He smiled at my surprise. "Mr. Jason, I am now 139 years of age." When I asked him to what he attributed his longevity, he answered thus, "You in the Western World are led to believe that you are born, must go to school, graduate, enter college, get a good job, work under high pressure, and at 65 you retire and prepare to die. You have all been brainwashed by very unhealthy teachings from very unhealthy people. You have a complete lack of understanding of life and death. A man does not get wise until he is 65. He has not absorbed everything he can until 80. He is 100 years of age before he can introduce into his daily life this wisdom and experience. He knows instinctively that he is what he thinks, as well as what he eats at this age. The next 40 years of his life are easy and happy. He has no fears of life, death or illness. Apart from an accident, he must remain healthy and productive because he eats and thinks properly. He has the right attitude toward everything. You in the West expect to die early, so you do. You really make no connection between yourselves and God. Of course, you are a part of God, and with this understanding only then do you realize that you do what you think you will do. Westerners expect to become ill periodically, so they do. They expect to die early, so they do."

"Try expecting to live long and be healthy. Combine this with the wisdom of living and you will do and become whatever you want. Nothing can stop you."

I asked him about the herbal tea and he told me that the monks use it constantly. "It's part of the settling of the mind and purifying of the body that we need in order that we may direct our thinking and our lives in the right direction."

I had noticed that the whole time I was there in the monastery the aged monks would take out a small package of powder and place some on their tongues. At last I ventured to ask about this, and the answer was in one of the most beautiful stories that I have ever heard.

It seems that when Bayan of a Thousand Eyes came out of Mongolia leading his great army, he brought with him hundreds of weak and wounded from continuous battles fought across the continent. After ravaging Peking, they proceeded on to the ancient city of Xian. Once there, the troops were amazed at the amount of very old, but agile and active people living in that town. They soon found that all the residents of that town took a special herb mixture every day without fail. Babies were fed this soon after they became three months of age. A small pinch of the herbs would be placed on their tongues.

The soldiers also found that this mixture was used only once each day after the morning meal, never at any other time. The local physicians started giving this to the weak and wounded soldiers, who soon found their strength returning very quickly. But something else was happening too. They also found that they felt better than ever before in their entire lives. Every soldier given this formula, according to legend, recovered. Legend also tells us that they all lived to a ripe old age.

The ancient gentleman leaned toward me and continued, "This herb mixture allows men to enjoy sexual relationships over the age of 100, and keeps their bodies trim, virile and strong, their minds active and alert. It also allows women to remain beautiful, feminine, and, above all, content into a very old age. That is why we like your formula so much, Mr. Jason, for it is very compatible with what we already are taking, although it serves a different purpose entirely."

Finally we come to Dr. Forbes Ross, who published his revolutionary book in London in 1912.

This man made quite a discovery. To all of his patients he would prescribe 60 grains of citrate of potash in distilled water. He realized that even then people desperately needed potassium to remain healthy. He discovered that in all of his years in practice he never had one patient come down with cancer. Also, the new patients that came to him with cancer were all well soon after taking the potash regularly.

We today suffer from potassium starvation, and it is interesting to note that if cancer is a "germ" disease, it has recently been found that potassium is nature's supreme antiseptic.

Interestingly enough, the "National Enquirer," March 1983 issue, claims that Karen Carpenter's death was caused by a very low potassium level due to her other problems with anorexia nervosa. I quote, "Low potassium levels cause irregular heartbeats which can lead to heart failure."

Potassium is needed as a daily supplement so I have added it to the Jason Winters "Take It For Health" list that is so popular in Europe.

Herbal Legacies

An eagle sat on his perch, high on the mountain, and gazed at the valley below. It was moving as though the whole earth was alive. It was in reality buffalo by the millions, all heading south for the winter.

A lone campfire raised smoke down by a small creek, and whenever a buffalo came too close he would be felled by many arrows shot by the Indian braves in hiding. At the same time, the squaws and maidens would be gathering herbs and preparing for the evening meal around the campfire. One herb they would pick was well known for treating swollen joints and fevers, another was for inner strength and well-being. These valuable herbs would be mixed with almost everything the women prepared.

This scene took place centuries before the first Spanish explorer tracked his way across the great American Southwest. Yet the women were well aware that they were practicing preventative medicine and also curing many ills.

There are few eagles left today, and hardly any buffalo.

The eagle now flies through polluted air, and drinks from heavily polluted rivers. But the knowledge of those ancient Indian women lives on and it is this knowledge and not modern science that will lead the few who will listen through to the new age in good health and safety.

At the same time that the eagle watched the great buffalo migration, another migration was taking place in an unheard of land half way around the world.

Long before the Chinese were invaded from the north, and long before the cities of Canton and Peking had their first settlers, China was ruled by the capitol city of Xian. The migration taking place here was to prove most important to the healers of all China, India and Tibet.

Powerful holy men, with a vast knowledge of herbal remedies, would travel far and wide to cities and villages, just for the honor of giving talks in the market places, imparting knowledge to the poor and ailing about how to regain abundant health and happiness.

Some of these travelling teachers found themselves in a far-off high country that would one day be called Tibet. They were excited to find that the rarefied air, due to the extreme elevation, was conducive to clear thinking and spiritual uplifting that allowed them a closer contact with God.

Because of this, many villages would spring up with their own monastery, filled with monks or holy men. Because they believed in reincarnation, (many lives) and the law of karma, (cause and effect) they were kind and gentle to each other. Each morning the villagers would lay at the gates of the monasteries baskets of medicinal herbs, which were used by the holy men daily.

Hundreds of years later, in 2838 B.C., the Chinese Emperor Sheng Noong would compile the world's first list of these herbs and their uses. He mentioned 365 herbs in all.

Long before the Mayflower reached America, and long before Ponce de Leon arrived in Florida looking for his fountain of youth, the Vikings sailed into natural harbors up and down the coast of North and South America, from Nova Scotia to Rio.

In South America they found the great rain forests and were overcome by the extreme dampness, the mildew and the rot that prevailed. Everything was covered with moss, fungus and insects. Everything that is except a certain type of tree that stood tall, strong and unblemished. No decay or fungus had touched this tree. No insects made their home in its bark. In this unhealthy climate this tree survived and was every bit as beautiful as the trees they were used to in far off Norway and Sweden.

The Vikings learned much from the natives of South America and when at last they were to turn their ships homeward, it was not gold and silver they would be taking back, but bark, bark that would bring a higher price than gold in their own land. For the voyagers had learned that since time immemorial this bark, made into a liquid, would successfully fight off all diseases and would greatly speed up the healing of accident victims. Medical scientists in South America have recently found that this bark contains a very powerful antibiotic. It is now famous world wide, (except in America) and is proving invaluable in many clinics and hospitals.

It makes no difference what ancient culture we wish to discuss, the fact remains that they knew something that we do not. They were closer to nature and closer to God. Their knowledge grew over thousands of years of trial and error until at last they knew the values of plants and herbs.

Concerning the billions of dollars spent by modern science the results prove that they have failed miserably. But they have succeeded in one respect!! They have certainly managed to keep the ancient knowledge written about here a secret in North America, where sickness and medication are the most expensive in the world.

The Thymus

For many years doctors thought that the thymus gland was just something that helped a child grow, and once an adult, then it served no further purpose. The thymus lies just beneath the upper breastbone in the middle of the chest. They thought that once the person became an adult, the gland should shrivel.

As a matter of fact, as recently as the early 1950s, if doctors came across a patient with a large (healthy) thymus they would give him cobalt radiation to try to reduce its size. Many brilliant doctors now know that the thymus is the seat of a person's immune system, and the only reason it grows smaller in most adults in America is because of stress and worry. Dr. John Diamond, in his new book "Your Body Doesn't Lie," has proven that you can tell a person's life force through testing the thymus. Beautiful thoughts, paintings, music make the thymus strong. Negative thoughts, ugly sights, and rock and roll music drastically weaken the thymus, and therefore your life force, almost instantly.

If you are jealous, vindictive, full of hatred, close-minded, then your thymus shrivels and you become weak. If a doctor tells you you're terminal, your body tests weak immediately. Just being with a negative person for a little while will leave you feeling weak and exhausted, while the negative person leaves feeling a little stronger.

Dr. Diamond says that he had never seen a sick person who did not have an underactive thymus. He believes that thymus weakness or underactivity is the cause of all illness.

Whether atheists like this or not, while in church, or praying, or helping some unfortunate person, your life force strengthens and your thymus becomes healthier.

One thing Diamond mentions is that if you have a group of people in a room, and suddenly someone lights up a smoke, within 20 minutes every person in that room will have the same level of nicotine in their blood. A frightening thought.

A sad plight in North America is the elderly. They are constantly told by their doctors, "Well, you can expect to be ill at your age," thereby sapping them continually of life force. Add to this the fact that we have been brainwashed into thinking that anyone of 70 years is old, (nothing could be further from the truth) and then the fact that if they do get ill their whole life savings goes immediately to the doctor and hospital, so that even if they recover from this whole negative attitude they have been put under, all they have to look forward to is a meager old age pension, where they can't even afford the proper nutritious food. As we are all only too aware, junk food is cheap, but nutritious food is almost out of reach for all of us. I wonder if anyone will ever do something about this tragedy. After living in the east I feel that our elderly are dying 30 years before their time, just because they have been told that it is expected. Because of this, I agree with Dr. Mendelsohn (M.D.) when he states that hospitals are very dangerous places to go. Not only are they rampant with disease, but the negative atmosphere literally destroys the life force of most people, especially the elderly:

Xian

After giving the formula to an English health food manufacturer I thought I would be free of the health food business. But then I was told about Xian, and I felt that everyone should know about this mixture at once. Both of these products are available freely, (but beware of useless imitations).

Xian consists of herbs that will reactivate the thymus, and you have just read how desperately we all need this. I call this formula Xian after the great Chinese capitol that was using herbs for healing thousands of years ago.

It is hard to believe that they knew about the thymus, the seat of life, and the life energy way back then. I am certainly very happy to make this my biggest and last contribution to my many friends around the world. Xian is destined, I have been assured, to be used widely by all people who wish to remain healthy and in a good frame of mind.

Peggy Mason is a spiritual writer living in Tunbridge Wells, England. She is highly psychic and has helped many around the world who just seem out of step with today's world.

One of her peeves is cruelty to animals. She claims that we do not get away with anything in this life, especially when we are cruel to defenseless animals. Today, for instance, chickens are raised, force fed in factories specializing in mass production. They are kept all their life in a small cage the same size as their body. No room to move at all, their head is fitted through a small hole in the cage and they cannot withdraw it, ever. They cannot run, move, scratch, or do anything but stand there, all of their lives. This pitiful, desperate, anxious, helpless, unhappy state causes poisons and toxins to course throughout the chicken's body. To eat such a bird simply transfers all that poison to the consumer. And we wonder why we get sick.

Mason also found that unnecessary operations on animals, done simply for practice and fun, have a direct effect on the perpetrator. She was horrified to find at one clinic, dogs living in utter terror because they had been operated on where an extra head was grafted on. In spite of the absolute cruelty shown them by man, the dog would still look at a stranger visiting and, with head hung low, would try to wag its tail.

Fortunately, these godless experimenters are not happy. According to research, although they somehow can justify this obscene occupation in their own godless minds, they do suffer far more illnesses than the average person. Cancer and heart disease strike them at a far greater rate. That is what is meant by "As you sow, so shall you reap."

Recently a doctor was so proud of himself while on TV. He explained that weeks before he had forced a white mouse into a tiny test tube and had sealed the end. A tiny hole was in one end so that the mouse could breath. He showed this on TV. The mouse, unable to move backward or forward could only in desperation turn over and over in a futile attempt to escape. The doctor was trying once again to prove that stress causes cancer. This has been proven hundreds of times already!

I was happy to note that the doctor had a serious case of

sanpaku which proved that his smiling face belied his true feelings, and could not hide his physical illness.

Now you may think that all this fuss over a mouse or chicken is ridiculous, but I say to you that just because an animal is helpless and can't talk doesn't mean that it has no feelings. It suffers just as much as you would under the same conditions. Participating in this type of experiment, or knowing about it yet doing nothing to stop it, causes a weakening of your life force and will eventually cause the same suffering in your own body, to an equal extent.

Cruelty is not conducive to good health. We can't get away with a thing in this life. We don't need a judge and jury to convict us, we do it ourselves. That is what God meant when he said "Judge not" for we need not judge and sentence others. Everyone, no matter how insensitive a person is, sentences themselves.

If you are sure you are going to die, then your thymus will shrivel and you will die. If you are sure, and have faith that you are going to live, then your thymus will expand and start your immune system working at a fast pace, and if you eat nutritiously, you will recover.

The whole of this book has been devoted to the story of one man's pursuit of life and of the desperation forced upon him by the death sentence passed by his medical advisors.

It has portrayed step-by-step the long march back to eventual triumph using God's abundant gifts of nature to put to flight a disease considered by much of the Western medical world as incurable.

Notes

Chapter 4

Guides To Good Health

The secret of Jason Winters' success lies wrapped within the mists of antiquity but it would be wrong to assume the only valuable aid to abundant good health comes from ancient times.

The story of GEROVITAL, the B-Complex formula developed by Professor Dr. Ana Asian of Romania, is without doubt tremendously impressive. As a beneficial remedy against the degenerative diseases of old age and maladies of the central nervous system this product (often foreshortened GH3) has a history stretching back 30 years-in more than 70 progressive countries and an estimated usage by upward of one hundred million people that cannot possibly be ignored. Bearing in mind safety and nonaddictive qualities of GH3 it can only be regarded as a most powerful and significant companion to TRIBALENE and XIAN for both remedial and preventative regimes.

Since Ruth Montgomery's new bestselling book "Threshold to Tomorrow" became available in every book store, Jason Winters has been deluged with mail each day. (The first chapter of Montgomery's book is dedicated to Jason Winters.)

Jason Winters Diet

Thousands Are Reaping The Benefits Of This Never-Go-Hungry Diet

BREAKFAST

Tribalene capsules with a glass of fresh juice. Two slices of whole wheat toast with Fleishmann's Margarine. Then take one XIAN capsule. (One Tribalene capsule for each 50 lbs. of body weight.)

LUNCH

For lunch, eat a can of Jolly Green Giant Asparagus, unheated. Asparagus acid has very beneficial effects on a person recovering from illness. Take two XIAN capsules after lunch.

SNACK

At three o'clock, have a light snack, a toasted cheese sandwich, while listening to good music. This relaxes you and eliminates Stress.

DINNER 7 P.M.

Take three Tribalene and three pancreatic enzymes 30 minutes before the evening meal. Then eat salad, fish or fowl, brown rice, lima beans, or a soft boiled egg (one), and any fruit or vegetable. Take one XIAN capsule.

COMPLETE BODY CLEANSE

SKIN

Hot shower, then cold. Dry off vigorously with a rough towel. Your skin will start to come alive and to breath again. Eat 20 raw, unblanched almonds each day for protein.

CELLS

Drink at least three glasses of distilled water daily. This will wash away the inorganic minerals surrounding and suffocating your cells. They will activate and come alive.

MIND

Listen only to good, soothing music. Try to understand poetry—it soothes the mind. Expect the day to be great and it will be.

NERVES

At five o'clock p.m., make a large glass of carrot juice and mix in two heaping tablespoons of Lewis Laboratory Brewers Yeast. Drink it down. It doesn't taste bad and you have just gotten all the Vitamin B-Complex that your body needs. Soon your nerves will be in good shape. That will allow your mind to be restful. Cancer patients should have an additional five glasses of carrot juice daily.

COLON

Healthy people need one soapy water enema each week. Ailing people should have one coffee enema each day. Three cups of black coffee, warm. Lay on right side and hold for 15 minutes. You will be cleansing the liver and colon this way. Coffee causes the liver to exude bile and so it cleanse itself.

Keep busy to avoid depression. Join a club, talk to a friend, use your phone.

If you are not working, then GET OUT OF THE HOUSE and go for a walk...for as far as you can, but not more than three miles.

STAY AWAY FROM NEGATIVE PEOPLE AT ALL COSTS. You cannot get well mentally with them draining you.

Never drink coffee or colas.

Cancer patients should take one 500 mg. laetrile tablet 30 minutes before each meal, after three pancreatic enzymes.

"A recent survey shows that one ounce of whiskey in a glass of hot water is good for everyone (except alcoholics)." Dr. Tan Pearce, Holistic Approach to Cancer.

A Word About Doctors

When I wrote my first book, I was pretty discouraged about doctors in general. I guess I had the misfortune of having atheistic, uncaring doctors and so had tarnished them all with the same brush.

During my hundreds of radio and TV shows, however, I am very pleased to say that I have discovered many dozens of medical men and women who do, in fact, care greatly about their patients. Some have even admitted to me that they pray sincerely for God's help before even attempting an operation.

Many have said that nutrition is the most vital treatment in all diseases. Even in the case of accidents, they say, proper nutrition is responsible for fast recovery. I am so glad to learn that there are so many caring doctors out there. It should make us all feel so much safer.

People like myself can tell you about things such as Tribalene and XIAN which I am sure will cut down your visits to doctors greatly. However, if you should need a doctor, look for one carefully. Make sure he believes in a power greater than the A.M.A. Even then, always get a second opinion.

"Over three billion people use herbs daily throughout the world."

Lord Beaverbook

"Hippocrates, the father of medicine, told all student doctors to use herbs for medicine."

Writings from the book "Hippocrates"

"The Lord Buddha told the Indian people 2,500 years ago that the weak should use herbs."

Writings of Buddha

"Jesus told the Essenes to purify their blood with herbs and all things will fall away."

Gospel of the Essenes

"Doctors and healers must work together toward their mutual goal to heal the sick."

"Alternative methods of treating illness should not be dismissed as hocus pocus."

Prince Charles, London Daily News 1983

This Is The Story Of Four Very Important Things:

1. **SELENIUM T**
2. **GOTU KOLA**
3. **TIBETAN SPICE**
4. **YOUR BLOOD**

Carefully mixing Selenium T, Special Spice and Gotu Kola together for the first breakthrough which we call Xian.

Since arriving in Tibet I have been light-headed. I am not sure whether it is due to the altitude or rather to the great amount of ancient wisdom given to me by my companion. It was from him, a man well over 100 years of age, that I learned how to eat, think, and be content.

It seemed strange indeed that an ex-terminal cancer patient like me should have to leave America, the scientific leader of the world, and go to far off Tibet to learn something as simple as "How To Live."

I could not help thinking that maybe we are the backwards ones. I am curious to find out why it is that an old man living in a small village in Tibet can tell me things that doctors, Scientists and highly intelligent men in America are just now discovering, and at a cost of billions of dollars. A person can return from Tibet with specific information on how to prevent and sometimes cure many of man's ills through herbs and diet. Secrets that have been tried and tested in Tibet for 5,000 years.

Some enthusiasts return to America ready to start right in helping people, only to be told a most definite "No" by one agency or another. It seems that a white-coated egghead must tie up the product for five years before he says it's okay. Something used for 5,000 years must now be tested by "one of us."

I am sure that many of us believe that God placed protection and cures for all man's ills right in or on the ground. All the herbs, minerals and vitamins are there, if we only knew which ones were which.

Many countries could help us in this respect. China, for one, has many thousands of herbalists who have been making people well for years.

Somehow our medical men and women are off on a tangent of their own and could not possibly ask assistance from any other than a medical man with the same training as themselves.

Can we really expect more from our medical people? Out of the many years of medical training that they receive, they get about one seven-hour course on nutrition. It should be the other way around.

Growing up in the West is not easy. There is no one to tell us how to eat, think, live. Anyone with the knowledge to help is frowned upon and discouraged. We certainly have a long way to go. If you don't think so then try going on a radio talkback show as a guest, and talk about an herb that can help sick people. Every doctor within 50 miles will call in and attack you as if you were the devil himself.

Because of this attitude, many truths are kept hidden. I think one of these truths concerns Selenium T.

1. Selenium T.

The ancient Tibetan and his friends and family eat a high selenium diet, and they just radiate health. It was because of his certainty about this mineral that I started looking into the research done on this element in the West. I think the results have been astounding, and certainly warrant the writing of this little book.

Selenium T, it could be just what you have been looking for.

In my travels around the world I discovered one very important fact. Every group of people who have a low intake of Selenium T suffer fatigue, depression, distressing menopause pains, and more susceptibility to all degenerative diseases, including cancer.

There is a direct relationship between highly civilized countries' processed foods, junk food and lack of selenium.

Selenium is an active mineral that is desperately needed in our bodies, for it is a wonderful antioxidant. It has been shown to prevent, or at least slow down, the aging process. Also, it has become famous in some clinics for slowing down hardening of the arteries. Males appear to need Selenium T even more than women. In the male, 50 percent of their body's supply concentrates in the testicles and the seminal ducts adjacent to the prostate gland. Also, much selenium is lost in the semen.

> *The levels of selenium in the blood of people in various cities has been found to bear a direct relationship to cancer mortality." The higher the levels of selenium, the lower the cancer death rate and vise versa.

Quoted from the* *"Vitamin Bible,"*** *Earl Mindell, author.*

Facts and Actual Test Reports

Because of a report given by Schwarz and Foltz, and encouraged by the same, Hopkins and Majaj showed that administration of selenium to children in Jordan with Washiorkor stimulated body growth and reticulocyte formation.

Burke reported finding in children from Guatemala with the same ailment, that although they did not respond to a nutritional supplement diet, the health of the children improved, and the concentration of selenium in their blood increased to control levels. These findings were confirmed by Levine and Olson.

In English this means simply that children in Jordan and also in Guatemala who were suffering a disease called Washiorkor were cured when selenium was added to their diet. Other diseases also responded when selenium was administered in small doses.

Periodontal Disease

Periodontal Disease is a major health problem in New England, a low selenium area, and has been reported to be associated with selenium deficiency in the sheep and cattle of New Zealand.

Sudden Infant Death Syndrome

The studies of researcher Money suggests that sudden death in human infants may result from the combined deficiencies of Vitamin E and selenium in cow's milk formulas. During the first month of life, breast-fed infants received more than 10 times the Vitamin E and more than twice the selenium than that of infants fed cow's milk formulas.

Cardiovascular Disease

Researcher Frost compared maps of early heart mortality and cardiovascular-related deaths for different areas of the United States and demonstrated an inverse relationship between ambient selenium levels and the death pattern.

Marjanan and Soni, who previously thought that manganese deficiency might underlie the very high cardiac and cancer mortality rate in Finland, have now adopted the view that selenium deficiency, prevalent all over Finland, may be the main contributor.

Lesions of selenium deficiency in rats and sheep have been associated with vascular abnormalities. Demonstrations of the role of selenium in maintenance of membranes may also suggest a function within the vascular system

Cancer

Investigation of the direct relationship of selenium to human cancer has been limited to demographic studies and to comparisons of levels of selenium in the blood of patients with or without malignancies, Chu and Davidson listed selenium compounds among potential antitumor agents. In addition, Shamberger and Rudolph and Shamberger, et al., associated protection from cocarcinogenesis with antioxidants (Vitamin E, selenium, etc.) and food preservation. Harr, et al., reported that concentration of dietary selenium delayed or prevented the induction of cancer by N-2-fluorenylacetamide (FAA). The effective concentration of dietary selenium in the torula feed in this experiment was the addition of 100-500 ng/g of feed.

On the average, the blood of cancer patients was reported to contain less selenium than the blood of other patients. However, the blood of other patients with some forms of cancer showed normal levels of selenium.

Mammary adenocarcinomas induced by FAA in selenium-depleted rats were more invasive than those induced in rats fed selenium-supplemented foods.

Above from the National Research Council

Reproductive System

When it comes to nutritional deficiencies, it seems to be that the reproductive organs suffer most. It is only fair to say that an excess of certain elements can cause just as much trouble in this area.

Selenium has done much to explain the distribution of this element in the reproductive system. This could mean that selenium has specific roles in the reproduction systems of male, female and developing offspring.

Kar and coworkers, and later others, found that the testicular damage induced by cadmium salts could be prevented by the administration of selenium dioxide.

It is the belief of many researchers that selenium transports cadmium away from vulnerable sites to other locus within the testes where it is innocuous.

Muth, et al. finds that administering selenium to pregnant ewes prevents myopathy in developing lambs. This has since been confirmed by many investigators.

It has also been confirmed through research that selenium does, in fact, pass from the pregnant mother to the unborn child.

Although selenium is present in cow's milk, human milk contains selenium in concentrations twice as high.

Because of the large amount of mercury used today by both industry and agriculture, the amount of selenium reaching the fetus might be diminished and thereby bring about a state of selenium deficiency in the child. Thus the advantage of breast feeding.

Deficiency in selenium definitely affects the general health. Rats fed a selenium-deficient diet over a few generations showed adverse effects on reproduction.

The female offspring failed to reproduce when mated with normal males. The male offspring had defects in their sperm-it was immotile (incapable of spontaneous movement).

In further studies on piglets from selenium-starved sows, it was shown that lesions appeared first in the connective tissue and capillaries.

Sprinkler found that rats starved of selenium suffered a thickening and degeneration in tissues such as the cardiac muscle, testes, and retina. Because of this, researchers Sweeny and Brown concluded that selenium deficiency causes primary damage to the vasculature (blood channels) and also had a bad effect on the membranes.

Selenium was found to be an anti-inflammatory mineral, which resulted in selenium tocopherol treatments for chronic lameness in dogs.

Researcher Money found that over 40 species of mammals and birds cannot tolerate selenium deficiency. It is all-important in their lives.

Selenium deficiency became an agricultural problem after World War Two because of the changes in animal nutrition. To deal with this the Food and Drug Administration approved the use of selenium as a food additive.

Although the importance of selenium in the case of animals is well known, little is known about its role in human beings. Reports from some laboratories indicate that selenium may have anticarcinogenic properties. Also, selenium has been found to have some inhibitory effect on the development of tumors in rodents injected with carcinogens.

Selenium is used as an antidandruff preparation and also as an antifungal agent in Tinea Versicolor.

Alternative therapy clinics around the world are using selenium in small doses to try to counteract degenerative diseases, and great promise is being shown.

2. Gotu Kola

The Second Ingredient

Gotu Kola has been used in many countries around the world, where they claim benefits, such as relieving mental fatigue, age spots, aging, brain problems, lack of energy, endurance, high blood pressure, poor memory, pituitary problems, senility, menopause and loss of vitality.

Revitalizes Your Sex Drive

This herb, mixed with the others mentioned, restores sexual desire and activity within just a few weeks. This approach is natural, with no harmful hormone injections or tablets. Doctors will not give hormones to people with cancer, or to those susceptible to cancer. If ancient Tibetans enjoy sex in their 90's and older, then why should we not be able to do the same?

It seems that Gotu Kola strengthens the mind, gives one the ability to cope with life and its stresses. Many say it gives renewed confidence and zest for life.

Many alternative clinics around the world are using this herb with success. Once carried from India on the backs of mules, this herb is now grown very successfully in Tibet, and is used both in Tibet and India for mental problems of all kinds. Combined with the vital spice from Tibet, we have Xian.

3. Spice From Tibet

Hundreds of years ago, a great army pushed its way across Mongolia, China and Tibet, raping and pillaging every foot of the way. In spite of confiscating all the poor farmers' crops, the soldiers were quite often very hungry and would have perished in the winter blizzards if it were not for the secrets passed down to them for thousands of years. One great secret was SPICE. Not just an ordinary spice, but one to give strength, purity and stamina. At night, while the weary soldiers slept, the "Physicians and Medics who were really herbalists, would scour the countryside looking for healing herbs.

The spice we call TIBETAN SPICE was really a find, for this particular herb was the one they knew would put all the soldiers who were feeling poorly, back into shape quickly.

It seems that even in those days there was such a thing as "sick call," which was held early in the morning before starting out on another long day's travel.

The herbalists were highly thought of and were carried all day between two horses. They slept mostly, and then at night, with the aid of large flaming torches, they foraged for herbs.

So highly thought of were these herbalist-physicians that during battle they were kept well to the rear in both luxury and safety.

Not only was it their job to treat wounds and help the fighting soldiers recover quickly, but they were also charged with keeping the whole army healthy. By this I mean that they had to practice PREVENTIVE MEDICINE. If too many soldiers came down with sickness other than wounds obtained on the battlefield, they would be severely reprimanded.

You see, in those days a physician's main job was to teach the solders how to keep well. What a wonderful way to look at the medical profession. To keep people well. To teach them how to eat, think and live correctly.

Even in those days they knew that preventing an illness was better than treating one, and so the spice mentioned here was treasured by all. This knowledge has been passed down to us today

Here is what modern researchers say about this particular SPICE.

"It is helpful if you want to burn the candle at both ends."

This miracle medicinal herb from early times reputedly cured a thousand ills and prevented the onslaught of old age. Greek doctors of old regarded this herbal spice as a sacred herb. Dioscorides used it as a remedy: Sore throats, snake bite, tuberculosis, kidney troubles, ulcers, arthritis, and lack of ambition and drive, among other things.

An old Arab proverb states, "How can a man die, with this spice available to him?"

Properly prepared it does away with decay, is good for the memory, makes a person stronger and prevents spiritual depression. "It makes the life force strong until the end," states another authority. This means that there is no degeneration of faculties during old age.

In MAN, it gives the other two ingredients a definite and powerful boost that cannot be denied. Grown in America, this spice can only be as good as the nutrients in the earth.

If the correct nutrients are missing, then the herb or vegetable has no good effect on the body. We in America, however, are content with growing food that looks good but in reality has no food value. We also shower the earth with poisons and chemicals to make plants grow quickly and larger than normal. Then quite often we polish the food with wax that is definitely detrimental to a person's health.

We, in actuality, end up eating something that looks great but is an almost "dead food" in our bodies.

Tibetan spice is carefully grown. It is cultivated in naturally rich soil, containing all the ingredients that God intended which are so necessary to our good health.

4. Life Is In The Blood

Every religion and culture has said that life is in the blood. For many years man has known that his blood, and the unrestricted flow of it in pure form through his body, was synonymous with good health.

Blood is, of course, the bearer of life for it carries oxygen and nutrients to every part of the body, while also removing poisons and gasses.

Vedic beliefs state that the flow of blood is actually the flow of life, for life is in the blood as it courses through our body. Stop the flow of blood to your foot and it dies quickly and the same goes for every part of your body.

For the blood also contains forces such as energy which our bodies receive from the sun. The spleen and the heart change these solar forces into usable energies which vitalize the body.

How obvious this is today. Give someone a blood transfusion from a sick person, someone for instance who has AIDS, and it will quickly kill the recipient.

The importance of the blood can be seen in the fact that when blood leaves the body, death occurs. When blood stops coursing through our veins, the same thing happens.

During the menstrual cycle, the flow of blood stops long enough to create another life. Ceremonies have been held for thousands of years idolizing the blood, shedding blood at human and animal sacrifices, smearing blood of freshly killed animals on the body to attract spirit entities that are said to be able to materialize by using the prana, energy of the blood.

The red mineral known as bloodstone has been used in ceremonies dating back 40,000 years and from all regions of the world. Blood stone is still used today as an antidote to bites, especially snake and other venomous reptiles.

In modern day society blood has been replaced by wine, and is now called the "Blood of Christ." Many people of the world believe that the blood controls the body through the soul that is in the blood. Through the thousands of years man has believed that blood is a kind of liquid fire and some reincarnationists believe that the blood holds a complete record of a spirit's hundreds of lives. Buddhists practice a system whereby a person can tell all about another human being by the color of that person's heart blood. Unhappy thoughts make the heart blood the deepest red, almost black. Happy thoughts make the heart blood bright red.

JUST ONE VICTIM

I recently had the misfortune of witnessing something that will live in my mind forever. As most readers know, I spend my time doing radio and TV shows and visiting cancer clinics.

I was at one such clinic the other day. A young man of 19 had thought it "cool" to smoke; he thought it made him look tough-and because he smoked a lot and took such big drags, he was accepted by his peers as a real cool character.

Not so when I saw him, however.

He had contracted cancer of the tongue.

The cobalt treatments had made things worse for him, and his tongue was so tender that it hurt to talk. He had been prepped for the operation to remove his tongue entirely, but the drug had not taken yet. I heard his screams first and when I looked around he was being wheeled down the corridor to the operating room. He was screaming, "Don't take me in there. Please don't take me in there." You see, he knew that once in that room, his tongue would be removed and, if he lived, he would never be able to do any more than drool and make strange noises. So much for being cool.

Another injection quieted him down. I did not wait any longer, but left the hospital.

Mentioned recently in a New York paper:

"More than 80,000 deaths each year are caused by infections caught while in the hospital."

According to the American College of Obstetricians and Gynecologists, "Up to 90,000 Caesarean sections could be avoided each year, considerably reducing the risk of maternal death, as well as length and cost of hospitalization." (Dr. Robert Cefalo, Committee Chairman, U.S. News and World Report, March 22, 1982.)

Not too long ago a medical doctor in New York stated on television that, "over 150,000 unnecessary operations are performed each year in America."

Are Americans deprived of natural remedies commonly accepted and used in other countries? They most certainly are. Fortunately, the organization known as the "National Health Federation," Monrovia, California, is fighting tooth and nail to remedy this.

Their fight on behalf of laetrile, Xian, enzymes, DMSO, chelation, Jason Winters' herbal tea and Freedom of Choice is well known.

Americans are told, for instance, that DMSO is worthless and yet...

In the year 1808 Russian lumberjacks, working in below freezing weather, discovered that if they rubbed DMSO (a product of trees) on their aching joints, the pain would quickly leave. Swollen arthritis would also disappear.

THE FOLLOWING WAS RECENTLY PUBLISHED IN A LARGE PENNSYLVANIA NEWSPAPER CALLED, "THE BULLETIN."

Has Jason Winters Really Got A Cure for Cancer?

"In the past few years a lot of attention has been given to one man's extraordinary solution to the terrible dilemma of cancer. His name is Jason Winters and the special capsules which he formulated have been sold worldwide to millions of enthusiastic believers.

This formula is now marketed in the form of capsules for greater convenience. Unlike the ordinary herb tablets manufactured by other competitors, the English who produce the unique Winters formula have somehow been able to turn out a product that can be easily crushed between the thumb and forefinger with very little effort to say the least. Try and do that with a regular herb tablet. In most cases, considerable pressure has to be used to even make the darn thing disintegrate properly in your hand. And in a few other instances, a hammer must be employed to pulverize the tablet to powder.

But not so with the Winters capsule. If it can be rubbed with minimal ease into powder by the fingertips, just think how much more easily it can be assimilated into the digestive system. It would not be farfetched at all to say that the capsule actually begins its immediate disintegration the moment it is swallowed and starts travelling down the alimentary canal to the stomach. No other herb tablet can work this swiftly.

The all-important question to ask however is, does Jason Winters' herbal tea really cure cancer? By examining its simple ingredients, we can learn the answer to this ourselves.

The first and most significant ingredient is, of course, chaparral. Well over a decade ago, this remarkable shrub captured the attention of the medical world for its extraordinary ability to cause tumor regression in some (but not all) forms of cancer. The literature proving this is too abundant to cite for lack of space here, but suffice it to say this herb has been more closely looked at for its strong anticancer properties than many plants of late have been. A man who has used this herb wrote to me some time ago of how it benefited him. Mr. Andrew Ranson of Oakland, Calif., testified that chaparral had successfully 'arrested' his leukemia. Another lady from Tempe, Arizona, Mrs. Kathalyn Windes, also contacted me several times about the great value this shrub has in the management of cancer. In neither case did the parties just mentioned use the word 'cure' but they did speak about the 'arrest' and proper 'management' of various kinds of malignant cancers in a responsible and truthful way.

"One could easily make claims for the Jason Winters formula in the cure for cancer. I'm quite sure that there are those who would be willing to testify under oath that Jason Winters' herbal tea has indeed cured them of one of Nature's most ravaging diseases. But, if you're like me, then you prefer that which is closer to reality That's why I feel comfortable with the words 'arrest' and 'properly manage' when describing the effects which Jason Winters' herbal tea can have on various kinds of cancer. After all, if it worked for Jason, then why shouldn't it work for someone else too?

Jason's other common ingredient is red clover. Jethro Kloss, America's greatest herbalist of the 20th Century, continually stressed the use of this fine herb throughout his book and especially in those sections where cancer is specifically mentioned. Of this wonderful herb, Jethro wrote: 'Red Clover is one of God's greatest blessings to man. I have used red clover blossoms for many years with excellent results. When I was a boy, my parents had me gather it for their postmaster who had a serious cancer. He lived to be an old man, without an operation.' (Back to Eden, p.301)

The final ingredient that makes up the unique Winters' package is a rare herb from Southeast Asia which Jason has romantically dubbed 'herbaline.' This precious spice not only gives the tea a different flavor but actually enhances the performance of the other two herbs and makes them work better. This synergistic effect is only achieved in the Winters formula. Other competitors have sought to imitate his formula with blends of their own, but to no real avail. The English, who Jason has officially authorized to manufacture his formula, spend the majority of their time with just his products alone. Unlike their other competitors, they can devote a lot of attention to turning out a high-quality product. But when other companies that already carry dozens and dozens of single herbs and combinations get into the act, it's mostly for monetary reasons. Why should they spend a lot of unnecessary manufacturing time on something so special as this when they've got an entire line of products to worry about. *So* they just crank out a cheap imitation of the real thing and peddle it along with the rest of their wares.

Unfortunately, such unethical practices as this are to be expected in the free enterprise system. This is why Jason and the people who make his products bear the family portrait, signature and J.W.T. to the Winters formula they make. This is to assure buyers of the genuine article and not some phoney reproductions.

When you consider what Tribalene contains, it is no wonder that so many people speak well of it in the health field today. Chaparral has been proven scientifically. And besides that, famous Amish writers, such as William McGrath, have spoken highly of the herb, too. In his 'Mountaineer Commentary' column of June 27, 1979, in "The Budget," McGrath not only praises chaparral for cancer but also specifically makes reference to Jason himself.

Thus, while we may refrain from using the definitive word 'cure' to describe Jason Winters' herbal tea, we can say, with all honesty and sincerity, that it does 'arrest' and 'manage' various kinds of cancer, not to mention all of the other wonderful health benefits it can also yield."

THE FOLLOWING IS TAKEN FROM THE WRITINGS OF MR. CARL RICHARDS, ENGLAND'S OLDEST LIVING PERSON, 113 YEARS OF AGE:

"Looking into Mr. Winters' report on Xian brought back memories of the time I resided In Lhasa, Tibet. I lived there from 1930 to 1938 and learned many of their health habits. Since that time I have consumed daily the substances that Jason Winters has joined together, Gotu Kola, Spice and Selenium.

I found that they must be taken in exact proportions, which always proved a difficulty, but now, with the advent of Xian, they are both measured correctly and placed in tablet form. I thank Jason Winters for doing something so wonderful, yet so simple. It has been said that the greatest breakthroughs will be the simplest ones, and Xian is no exception. I believe that these ingredients are necessary to maintain life, and today so many people are drastically lacking them that they are leading what I call 'half lives,' I am alive today because I visited the Himalayas and Tibet and learned these truths. Now Jason Winters is doing what I should have done 45 years ago, and that is to make this knowledge available to everyone."

Hope Is Your Most Valuable Asset

The medical profession's biggest argument against any alternative therapy, including laetrile, enzymes, DMSO, Jason Winters herbal tea, any herbs, nutrition, faith, etc's, that it gives a patient false hope.

There is no such thing as false hope. One of the wisdoms learned in Tibet is that words spoken to a sick person are like a weapon. Words spoken by a person's God-like doctor are taken for granted to be true.

How many times have you heard a doctor say, "We've done all we can, the rest is up to the patient. He must have the will to live."

The doctor is saying, in effect, that if the person has the will to live, then their chances are much better, Why is it then, especially in the case of cancer, that doctors send people home with "just three months to live?"

Don't they realize that just by saying that, they actually cause it to happen? They have taken away all hope, have superseded even Jesus when he said, "Faith can move mountains."

Tibetans believe that if a person has faith and hope, his

body manufactures certain chemicals that aid in the curing. But if the patient is convinced that he will die, then his body manufactures chemicals to fulfill his belief.

Every religion in the world says it. Even our parents and school teachers said it: "If you want to do something bad enough, nothing can stop you."

History books are full of people who won out against all odds. Every hero that we have ever heard of did this and every man, woman, and child is capable of "winning out" regardless of their circumstances.

This is what the famous book "The Power of Positive Thinking" was all about. It's what the Bible is all about.

If you have an inferiority complex, you go to a psychiatrist and he tells you over and over again (under hypnosis) that you are as good as, if not better than, anyone else. Finally you believe it and so you are cured.

If you constantly tell a child he is stupid, then eventually he believes it and so acts stupid. Encourage the same child every day by saying he is bright and will achieve, and he will. It is all so simple, yet the medical profession still keeps on handing out death sentences.

I believe that when a person is very ill, they hang on to every word their doctor utters. I have seen the excitement that rushes through a person's body when the doctor says, "You're going to be all right."

I have seen the person fall apart and die quickly when the doctor pronounces the death sentence. All of us must be careful of the words spoken to the sick. Jesus says that miracles can happen. So how can we dare, even if we are the most educated and intelligent doctor in the land, to call Jesus a liar and to thereby quicken the death by weeks, months, or maybe years?

THE MIRACLE OF PURE WATER

The sun shines on the sea and lakes, causing vapor to rise and form clouds. This vapor is pure. It leaves behind all bacteria and, what's even more important, inorganic minerals. Inorganic minerals can not be used by the body. Rain water, travelling over limestone and other minerals in the ground carry these minerals to plant life. The plants, vegetables, fruits, etc., then use these inorganic minerals for food, changing them into organic minerals. This is when the human body can use them to advantage. These are the minerals necessary for our good health.

Rain water is no longer pure because it has to fall through layers of filthy air, and because distilled water acts as a magnet for toxic materials, by the time it hits land, it is also toxic.

Hard water, or any water other than distilled water, is full of lime salts, calcium, magnesium, sodium, iron, copper, silicon, nitrates, chlorides, viruses, bacteria, chemicals, and many other inorganic materials detrimental to the body. Over five billion tons of dissolved minerals are washed into the sea every year. Because of this, sea life has been reduced 50 percent over the last 30 years. Pesticides and factory waste are responsible for most of this.

Many thousands of people are under the false impression that bottled water or filtered water keeps them safe. Treated bottled water does kill the bacteria, but does not remove the minerals that are just as harmful.

If you have a private filter that you use, it still only removes bacteria, leaving the harmful minerals. Plus, some experts say that a filter only works well for the first two days, then turns into a breeding ground for bacteria, thereby defeating its own purpose. Also, experts say, treated bottled water is full of dead bacteria which, although not directly causing illness, does definitely set the groundwork, entering the body and eventually acting as a compost heap or fertilizer for bacteria to grow and spread.

The idea of drinking water was originally to flush poisons from the body, washing every cell daily. Each living cell in our body is a life of its own. It needs to take nourishment from the blood and expel poisons. Imagine, if you will, that inorganic minerals that you have been consuming since birth in your water supply have surrounded almost every cell of your body, making it impossible for the cell to do its job properly, if at all. This is degeneration, illness and death, not only to that particular cell, but to you as a person.

Throw drinking water on a glass or mirror, and when it dries you are left with spots That is the inorganic materials that are even now surrounding each cell, making it difficult to live a normal, healthy life. Take distilled water and do the same. You will find that it leaves no spots at all.

Well water is every bit as harmful, but there is good news at last. Start drinking distilled water, and only distilled water. It makes everything taste better. Also, it acts as a magnet in your body, leeching out all of those harmful minerals that have been accumulating around every cell since the day you were born. It washes every cell and, I think, because of the thousands of testimonies I have read, will do away with aging and most ills. Water distillers are available in many sizes, and we consider ours as the most important appliance in our home, making our lives so vibrant and happy. Try distilled water for one month and you won't believe the results. Xian works well, but with distilled water it is dynamite. Every group in the world known for longevity has access to pure water with no minerals. It truly is a Godsend.

Notes

Chapter 5

The Lowder Colonic Board

I had just finished reading the famous book "Back to Eden" written by that most brilliant herbalist Jethro Kloss. I had been particularly interested in page 144 explaining high enemas. It was made abundantly clear to me that whatever a person does to regain their health, it doesn't mean a thing if you have a dirty colon.

I had lunch that day with Eldon Lowder and mentioned to him about the importance of the colon. He perked up immediately and for the rest of the meal spoke at great lengths about rotting fecal matter lodged in people's colons sometimes for 20 years. He said the colon was the cause of most disease, being dark, damp and warm, a perfect breeding ground. He wondered why I didn't order dessert, then said, "I have designed a perfect high colonic board which people are raving over. It is strong and comfortable and allows people to thoroughly clean their colon with ease, in the privacy of their own bathroom." I was surprised because I had always thought that this cleansing had to be done by a professional.

He told me of a friend who had thought he was healthy but decided to try Eldon's colonic board. On the third time of using, the friend called Eldon to say that he had passed particularly vicious looking worms. Eldon then reached across the table to ask if I would like to finish up with some hot chocolate, which I refused. He continued that because of the curved design of the board, there was no splash back, therefore eliminating the threat of vaginal infections. I now own one of these specially designed colonic boards and in all honesty I must admit that, in spite of all the enemas I had taken since terminal cancer, I was very surprised at the results. To know that you have a clean colon is very reassuring. Eldon Lowder is most successful today, and ships his colonic boards far and wide.

* * * * *

The old man squatted in the dust beside me and as we gazed down the street of cages in Bombay, he began to speak. "You see, my son, this life is an illusion—it simply prepares us for the real life in spirit—the eternal, everlasting, ever conscious life beyond the grave. Without loss of awareness we are there, free, happy and painless, happy in the complete knowledge that life is everlasting."

His sparkling eyes shone from amidst a thousand wrinkles, and he whispered "this great truth is hidden from man for fear he may try to reach the spirit world too soon. He must do his schooling on earth first."

Tears came to my eyes as I realized that I had always known this truth. Deep inside, we all do.

Book Two

In Search of the Perfect Cleanse

CHAPTER 6

INDIAN ATTACK

The Indians had been attacking the wagon train all morning and Audie Murphy was doing a great job picking them off, one by one. The director called for a lunch break and we all gathered around the chuck wagon—all that is, except the Mexican Indians. They started their usual fire and began making the cactus tea they drank every day.

How we sophisticated whites would laugh at them while we gorged ourselves on jelly doughnuts, coffee with sugar and cream and lots of cigars. I had no way of knowing that this special scene would one day, 30 years later, help to save my life. For what all these Indians were doing was purifying their blood on a daily basis, with an herbal tea.

In 1976, when I recovered from terminal cancer, I visited Tibet, the "rooftop of the world." The monastery I stayed at was populated by men all 50 years my senior or more. I learned more from them about health, happiness and longevity than I could ever have learned from one of New York's top oncologists. For they too know about purifying the blood.

It seems that God placed a certain herb on each continent to purify a person's blood so that their natural immunity could "take care of any disease and heal the body."

God did not just throw us down here saying, "There's 10,000 fast food restaurants, go to it." He gave us an immune system that allows the body to heal itself, However, it can't do this as long as our blood is so toxic. We have forgotten that it's natural to be healthy and unnatural to be unhealthy We have been brought up to believe it's the other way around. This kind of negative thinking brings about disease. Expecting to be ill causes illness.

The old man in Tibet said it quite plainly, "Tell the Americans to try expecting the best for themselves, tell them to expect a happy day, a long life, and a happy one, for you create your own environment."

The art of imagery bears this out and is now in use in alternative health clinics around the world. It has been proven that patients can "will" their immune systems to attack the illness or tumors. When it comes to cancer, however, we have a doubly hard job, for we have been so brainwashed by thinking that cancer means death. It's not their fault of course, for from birth we hear about Aunt Nellie dying of cancer, Humphrey Bogart dying of cancer, Hubert Humphrey, John Wayne, and on and on. No wonder when our white-coated genius looks at us and says "cancer;' we start dying right away,

The Chinese know that when all hope is taken from a person they start dying. Tell that same person that they will live and their body secretes certain chemicals to obey that belief. Doctors call everything that they don't understand, "false hope." Well, I want to tell you that there is no such thing as false hope. Hope is faith and faith can move mountains, so what can it do to a silly little tumor?

I know that you can probably tell me how many people die of cancer each year in America. But I bet you can't tell me how many people beat cancer and go on to live healthy, happy lives. I have made it my business to find out, and we are thousands strong.

You know, voodoo only works if the victim is told of the curse against him. His mind does the rest. He dies even though quite healthy. Following this thought, how many old movies have you seen where the doctor tells the family, "We have done all we can for Aunt Nellie, the rest is up to her. She must have the will to live." Were the doctors telling us that if we had the will to live we could?

Your mind could be more powerful than you think. It could be responsible for your exact condition today, including health, wealth and happiness. Doctors tell us that when cancer is diagnosed, they mentally write the patient off. Unfortunately, so do the family and friends. Because of these negative vibrations it's pretty hard for someone still in shock over learning they have cancer to pull themselves together and prove the world is wrong, but thousands are doing it. We don't care if the medical profession calls it spontaneous remission or not. People are living and that's the bottom line.

What Has Gone Wrong?

He started by asking the above question Then, without waiting for an answer, he continued. First of all, we can't blame doctors or food manufacturers because our problem started 10,000 years ago. If our Saviour had been on earth in those days, he would have been warning us of the problems involved with agriculture. At that time we changed from being hunters into herders and agriculturists. When we were hunters we had to run, stalk and skin our food and, because of all this work, we did not get fat, but always stayed in top shape. If we did get fat, we could not catch our food so we did not eat, which meant we got thin so we could then run and catch our food. It is interesting to note that they had healing people even in those days. As a matter of fact, there are some historians who believe that doctors or healing persons have been around for over 50,000 years. Because people in those days had no permanent home, they had no pollution problems. They tended to move around in groups following their food, to higher ground in the summer and so on. It comes as a surprise to many to find out that people started using fires to cook their food well over 300,000 years ago, but as recently as 10,000 years ago cooking was only for meat and they would eat whole foods. Grains, grasses, fruits and animals were consumed in their entirety. Foods consumed in their entirety seem to be balanced by nature, and are healthier for the body than the food we eat today. Scientists have separated herbs, grains, etc., and the natural balance has gone. All the food in those days was alive also. After all, when a tiger runs down a rabbit he does not carve off a leg and store it for next week, but rather he eats it even though the rabbit is still alive. When fish eat each other, they are alive. Grains and herbs were gathered and consumed, then the people moved on to another abundant supply. They did not gather and store the food which would have meant that after a while they were eating dead food. They did not know about agriculture, the art of producing corn or wheat on the same field year after year, of using tons of fertilizers then of cutting and storing food for the future. Agriculture in this respect is bad. It showed us how to mass produce food in ground that natural chemicals and goodness has long since disappeared from. The food looks good but has very little value. Of course, nowadays, it must be sent to the supermarket to sit for weeks until we buy it. By this time it is totally dead, but something else even more deadly has been added to it along the way. Preservatives. We are only now finding out how deadly this type of agriculture and preserving can be. The country that does the most of these two things suffers the most, has far more sickness and early deaths.

Plus, don't forget the psychological effects. Ten thousand years ago it took a person only two hours each day to get enough food to fill his stomach. The rest of the time he had to himself to do whatever he wanted to do. How many of us today can get by on just two hours work per day?

The food they ate was highly diversified also, and it was nontoxic. Anything they ate that made them feel a little sick right away, they stayed away from it in the future. The effect was immediate. Today, however, due to agriculture and preservatives and dead food, the effects are slow and actually kill us over a long period of time, so that we can't place the blame on any specific thing.

For instance, if you wish to poison mice in your house, you have to kill them the first try. If the poison just makes them sick they automatically know enough never to touch that food again.

In England they teach foxes not to attack sheep by poisoning a leg of lamb and leaving it for the fox to stumble upon. The fox gets sick and will never touch sheep again.

We in modern society have doctored up our food so that it

looks good and tastes good but, in actuality, it is dead food that is slowly killing us. We have lost the natural reflex that animals still have.

With our GOD-given self-healing power within each of us, it takes 25 years of poisoning ourselves daily for us to become ill; and because of the long time lapse, it is impossible to connect the exact cause of our degeneration and early death. One hundred years ago, eight percent of our food was dead; 50 years ago 22 percent of the food we consumed was dead, today 75 percent of everything we put in our mouths is dead.

It is not only our bodies that we are destroying either, but the very air we breathe and the water we drink. If man were to cease to exist on earth today, it would take 50 years for the air alone to become pure again. It does not matter if we live in a remote farming area, for air pollution and acid rain is now everywhere.

Today we do not have the variety of foods that we had 10,000 years ago. We have the same few foods that have been made to taste different. Breakfast cereal is almost the same, yet sold under hundreds of names and flavors, all of which are dead.

In short, any food that man has fooled with is bad for you. There are well over a half a million trace additives and chemicals known to man and it is very reasonable to assume that during the course of a week we consume all of them. These trace elements are both dangerous and difficult to get rid of from your body. Has it ever occurred to you that we feed our animals better than ourselves? Look at all the signs in the zoos stating, "please don't feed the animals." They are there because they don't want the animals to become ill eating such garbage.

It is wrong to say that people who enjoy health foods are going through a fad, for nothing could be further from the truth. Are they not just trying to continue the way of eating that man has become used to over 50,000 years? By the same token, we can't say that alternative therapy is really alternative. After all, the so-called alternative therapy has been around since the beginning of man. It's medicine and drug companies which are relatively new which are in effect the alternatives.

You see, we now have to get more food per acre than we used to. Because of this we use fertilizer which contains nitrogen, potassium and phosphorous but none of the trace elements needed to make the crop nutritious. Fertilizer assists the land in producing food that looks good and in large quantities, but of extremely low nutritional value.

Our soil is deteriorating steadily, and will continue to do so. In China, however, they have managed in their own natural way of farming to keep up the quality of soil. Now, with our fertilizer and agriculture experts visiting China in order to get big sales, the soil quality of that land will quickly deteriorate. What will inevitably follow is illness of the Western kind which China is at present relatively free of.

Did you know that the average American consumes over 190 lbs. of sugar each year, most of which is hidden in dead food but added just for taste, to get you and your children "hooked" on it and all for a profit to the manufacturer. We all know that sugar is a killer. One hundred years ago the average consumption was five pounds per year. During any war there is usually a shortage of sugar, and babies born during wartime have proven far more healthy than those born at any other time.

To give you an example of the long term effect of bad food, let me state the following: Dr. Burkitt of England found that Blacks of South Africa, eating natural food, had an incidence of diabetes of only three people out of 45,000. The same tribe today, after consuming Western food for 30 years, has an incidence of diabetes amounting to 15,000 per 45,000 population.

Mr. Hoffer, that genius of nutrition, discovered that in America one third of the people admitted to a hospital were suffering from malnutrition. After seven days in the hospital, however, over two-thirds of the patients suffer from malnutrition. The only answer to this is to eat as little as possible while in the hospital, except fruit and vegetables brought in by family and friends.

Interview With Zurich Health Magazine August, 1984, Switzerland

I finally tracked down Jason Winters at the Palace Hotel in Bern where I phoned for an appointment. The idea was to do a story on a man who had managed to cling to life for eight years with terminal cancer. I had read the report that he should have died seven and a half years previously.

I was not prepared for the man himself, however. I met him in the lobby of the hotel and my shock evidently showed, for Mr. Winters laughed and told me not to worry, he was used to it. I must tell the reader that I was shocked because I had readied myself to meet an old, tired sick person, underweight, with no hair, and barely clinging to life.

Jason Winters, however, was a giant of a man, healthy, suntanned, smiling and happy with an air of easy calmness about him. His full head of hair was cut in a style that made him resemble Cary Grant. He explained to me that he jogged, lifted weights, and swam regularly.

Who would have guessed that Winters, British born, one-time Hollywood stunt man, was down to only a few weeks to live back in 1977 with a massive neck tumor known as infiltrating squamous cell carcinoma? But that was three million copies of his book "Killing Cancer" ago.

His treatment for throat, jaw and neck cancer is fully documented. His response to cobalt therapy and the suggested surgical mutilation of his neck and face are also documented.

It was because Winters suffered from the radiation therapy and was horrified at the suggested removal of his tongue, jaw bone and radical neck dissection (that may prolong his life for a few weeks) he decided to do something.

Doing something meant trips to Asia, where the Lord

Buddha 2,500 years ago had told the Indian and Chinese people to use "herbalene" (a special herb) for their tumors. To Arizona, where the Indians have used a special herb (chaparral) to purify their blood for centuries. And lastly to Europe where the gypsies have been using yet another herb for the same purpose (red clover), as mentioned by Jesus in the Gospel of the Essenes, taken from the Dead Sea Scrolls. Jesus evidently said, "Purify your blood with herbs and all things will fall away"

Winters, in a state of both shock and terror, started reading religious books, preparing himself to meet his maker. "One thing stuck out like a sore thumb," he told me excitedly, herbs for health are mentioned 23 times in our Bible and herbs for health are mentioned in absolutely every faith since the beginning of time. It was too great to be just a coincidence."

"The more I read, the more the simple fact came screaming through to me. God placed an herb on each continent to do just one thing, and that is to purify a person's blood. Once a person's blood is pure, then fresh oxygen and nutrition can get to every part of the body. Suddenly a person's natural immunity starts to work and the body heals itself of disease. God did not just throw us down here and say There's 10,000 fast food restaurants, fluoride in the water, preservatives in your food, microwave ovens, stress and war—have fun!' He gave us an immune system to fight off disease and all it needs is a little help.

"When I went to Asia, North America and Europe looking for these special herbs, I found that they did not work for me until I mixed the three herbs from the three continents together. In Biblical times any one of these herbs would have worked to purify a person's blood, but that was before fluoride and junk food. Today it takes the combined efforts of the three herbs to work.

I think that the secret message that is hidden in every religion, and has been overlooked is that 'Life is in the blood. The blood of Christ' and so on. It worked for me and suddenly I started getting an awful lot of unwanted publicity about it. Everyone wanted to know my story."

Forced to Act

"I must tell you that I was scared. I was not prepared to take on the billion-dollar drug companies, the medical associations and doctors, all of whom would chew up and spit out anyone who would dare to even say that possibly, just possibly, herbs can help. Even though, of course, Hippocrates, the father of medicine, told all the student doctors to use herbs for medicine.

Listen, I was just glad to be alive, I didn't want to enter a war with the biggest business in the world. They would not let me alone, however. Letters would pour in, reports on radio and TV kept popping up about my case. At last I gave the formula away to the Xian Corporation in England. It was kind of like giving away the formula to Coca-Cola. I had no idea that millions would soon be using it just as a kind of preventative health product.

I was amazed the other day to hear from one of England's top doctors that when I mixed the three herbs together, one of them, the herbalene, acted as a catalyst and made the other two far stronger. This was all by accident on my part because in those days I was so busy drinking and carousing and having fun that I didn't even know what a catalyst was."

The Famous American "CHOICE" Magazine, August 1984, put it this way:

"Extensive anecdotal information has for years linked both chaparral and red clover to anti-cancer activity. Indeed, the anti-cancer ingredients nordihydroguaiaretic acid-NDGA has been isolated from chaparral tea, an elixir of the American Southwest.

Herbalene may in fact be Astragalus membranaceous and Ligustrum lucidum, herbs widely used in a collective Chinese immune- stimulating therapy called Fu-zheng, information on which was provided, amazingly enough, in 'CANCER,' a publication of the American Cancer Society, in 1983."

Herbs Do Not Cure Illness

Evidently there are millions of people in almost every country of the world taking this formula daily. It is in capsule form and is named TRIBALENE. It is already quite popular in Switzerland. I was surprised to hear Winters state the following, "I do not believe that herbs cure any illness. I believe that they merely purify the blood and help the body get strong enough to heal itself."

Winters also surprised me further by stating that he was not against orthodox medicine and doctors; "Everyone has their place, and we must all work together for the benefit of mankind. I find doctors very helpful and understanding. Of course, we do not claim to cure anything and if I fell down today and broke my leg, I would go to the hospital immediately."

"My whole family and I have medical insurance of course, but when it comes to cancer or any other degenerative disease, then I think a nutritious diet, along with special herbs, helps tremendously."

When I mentioned to Winters that I had read his book "Killing Cancer," now available in the German language, and had found it fascinating reading as well as thought provoking, he replied, "The biggest surprise to me was when the publisher asked me to write this book, saying he would pay me 26 cents U.S. per copy. I thought I would be lucky to make $26, but as you know, it's already sold nearly twelve million copies worldwide. Even doctors are buying it for their patients who have lost all hope.

Does Not Always Work

When asked if he thought that this TRIBALENE formula worked for everyone and everything, he replied, heavens no.

The biggest trouble we have is people expecting that it will and being shocked when it doesn't. For instance, someone has terminal cancer, has undergone chemotherapy and radiation, but this did no good so their doctor has sent them home to die as a hopeless case. These people suddenly hear about Tribalene and expect it to work in every case. Miracles do happen and a change of diet, thinking, life-style, and blood purification often have great effects, but it is unfair to expect anything to work every time. Plus, I believe that often it's just a person's time to go. On the other hand, we hear of thousands of cases of what the doctors call spontaneous remission."

Hope And Faith

Winters' deep feelings of hope and faith are well worth mentioning here. I asked him if this new approach to degenerative disease would give people false hope; Winters' reply was simply, "What new approach? If Jesus, Krishna, Bahaii Uhila, Hippocrates talked about it and if two-and-a-half billion people of the world believe it, and have practiced it for centuries, how can you think it's new?"

He continued, "There is no such thing as false hope, for hope is faith and faith can move mountains. If faith can move mountains then think of what it can do to a silly little tumor! Many scientists feel that when a person thinks he is going to die, their body secretes chemicals to obey that belief. On the other hand, when a person thinks he is going to live, the body secretes another type of chemical to obey that belief. You see, we are all part of God and because of that our thoughts are more powerful than you can imagine. These chemicals are called endorphins and endocrines, and this has been proven by many people around the world. If all hope has been taken away, if you are sure you are going to die, then you will, without a doubt.

Cancer Does Not Mean Death

"People, especially in America, have been brought up to believe that cancer means death. When a child they heard that Aunt Agatha died of cancer, then John Wayne, Humphrey Bogart, Hubert Humphrey, Ingrid Bergman, and on and on. Naturally, when your doctor tells you that you have cancer, you start dying right away and that's usually the end of it. I really believe in mind over matter.

"Most people know that 1,000 people each day die of cancer in Europe, but how many can tell us the amount of people who recovered from cancer? Not many, but I can because I have made it my business to know There are thousands alive today who should have died but are now back at work leading happy, healthy lives. For some strange reason they are well in spite of everything."

I mentioned to Winters that I heard him yesterday on a local radio show, talking through an interpreter, and had heard him say that his biggest troubles were with some born-again Christians. I asked him to explain: "This is only a problem in North America. We have small groups of small-minded people, living in small towns, going to a small church and listening to their small-minded preacher telling them his version of the Bible. His interpretation. They believe it 100 percent. They forget that God said 'Judge not, less ye may also be judged' and also 'Let he that is without sin cast the first Stone.' These people call anyone who does not agree with everything they say 'non-Christians.' They say that four billion people in the world are wrong and that they are right. In fact, they cast stones at everyone. They have forgotten about watching out for false prophets and are perfectly content to risk their eternal soul on that silly little man in the pulpit. Because their preacher does not believe in Buddha, Krishna, Bahaii Uhila, Hippocrates, or the Gospel of the Essenes (That gospel was removed from the Bible in the year 503 A.D. so that the churches would have a better hold on the congregations). All the things the world believes in, they do not. They love saying that a person is not a Christian. Their sin of judging others bothers them not at all. One day a person in their congregation with terminal cancer decided to try herbs. He had nothing to lose as he was definitely dying. He tried herbs but died anyway. Suddenly this congregation started attacking herbs, healthy diet and so on, just because these things do not work all the time.

"It is impossible to be evil without paying for it with your health, emotions and mind. Judge not means that we should not judge people. We don't need to. The spiritual people advance in perfect health and the evil ones destroy themselves."

I left Jason Winters sitting in the lobby of the hotel sipping herbal tea with the hotel manager and, as I drove the highway back to Zurich, I went over again all the things he had told me. He made no claims, he didn't believe that herbs cured disease, but rather just purified the blood. He believes in faith and eternal hope, he was a devout Christian, but most of all, he was the healthiest, tallest, most handsome person I had encountered in a long time.

The world will hear much from this man in the years ahead.

Adolph Schloss
Zuhealthmag

. . . .

Notes

Chapter 7

Suppressed Therapies

Have you ever wondered what happens to all those so-called "miracle products" that receive publicity in one national newspaper or another, then you never hear of them again?

Usually the publication gets into a lot of trouble for printing it in the first place, then all future publicity is stopped. The persons selling the products are usually tricked or entrapped into a phoney suit about "practicing medicine without a license" or if they can't stop them that way, they attack them on some income tax charge or other.

The following story indicates a selection of natural products that fall into the above category. Freely available in other countries, especially in socialized medicine areas, they are almost unobtainable in North America

Erik Gudme Of Denmark
A Remarkable Cancer Case

The bombs had been falling all night, and the Nazi anti-aircraft guns had kept all of the population of Copenhagen awake.

Erik Gudme had even more problems to worry about than the bombs, for the day was April 11, 1942 and it was his day to get the results of his medical examination. He felt very ill indeed as he made his way down the Frederiksberggade to the doctor's office. His doctor was a kindly old Jewish man who had plenty of troubles of his own in this German-occupied city.

The news was all bad. Erik had cancer in two places in his colon, one in the ascending colon and another growth in the descending colon. A spot on his liver looked highly suspicious, and there was a tumor the size of a small egg in his right lung. According to the doctor, the disease had been progressing for over four years. Erik's heart sank with complete and utter despair, and he cried openly in the doctor's office. At this the doctor went to his waiting room and sent all the other patients home, so that he could spend some time with this most distraught person.

The doctor's compassion, guidance, confidence and assurance at last penetrated Erik's fear, and thank God it did, for when Erik left the man's office three hours later; he took with him the information that would save his life. Erik died of natural causes in January of 1983 at the age of 85 years

He was never to see that old Jewish doctor again, for he was killed in an explosion soon after, but he certainly lived on in Erik's mind. The information Erik received that day is still as potent and valid today, and it can really work for you, if you trust it. It is as follows:

"Don't let any man tell you when you will die for that is up to you, your mind and your God. Don't let any man run your life. You must always remain in control. Never let anyone talk you into an operation. You must want the operation and have faith that it will work first. Otherwise do not have it.

"Do not be overpowered by sophisticated medical men, for more people die from the mistakes of these men than from their illness. Remember Erik, no man can make you do anything for you belong only to God. It is quite permissible to leave the hospital 10 minutes before an operation if you should wish to do so. Most people feel that they are captured once in a hospital. They feel that they must subject themselves to anything. This is wrong. Do not hand yourself to anyone else and expect them to cure you with a pill, for you must heal yourself. Now Erik, eat every day four cloves of garlic, press carrots and drink the juice. Eat or drink red clover as there is a strange goodness in the Danish kind. (Tribalene has an abundance of this.) Never go for a day without having a bowel movement. Red clover or coffee enemas will clean your colon and heal your liver. Eat no white flour, red meat or dairy products ever again. Eat many apricot kernels each day (15) and have lots of fruit. If you do these things Erik, then you can live longer than I."

(The Jason Winters diet includes all of the above.)

YUCCA

The Food Supplement That Helps Prevent And Treat Arthritis And High Blood Pressure

By Shideler Harpe

"We've known for several years that a food supplement extracted from yucca can be remarkably effective in preventing, eliminating and reducing the pain, swelling and joint stiffness suffered by arthritis victims. Now there is indisputable evidence that this natural plant substance can prevent and lower high blood pressure, high cholesterol, and high triglyceride levels in the blood. We seem to only have scratched the surface of the medical uses of yucca."

Robert Bingham, M.D.
"Arthritis News Today"

The nation's estimated 50 million arthritis victims received encouraging news four years ago when a medical team reported that a natural plant substance had proven effective in relieving the pain, stiffness and swelling of some kinds of arthritis. Doctors reported that a food supplement, an extract made from the yucca plant, contained a natural substance which often acted like cortisone on the swelling and pain of arthritis, but it did not cause any unpleasant or harmful side-effects.

In a 12-month controlled study at the National Arthritis Medical Clinic in Desert Hot Springs, California, doctors found more than 60 percent of the 149 patients monitored by the medical team reported varying degrees of relief of pain, stiffness and swelling of arthritis without any ill effects whatsoever. Further testing in 1978-79 has confirmed findings of the previous report and has also indicated that the yucca treatment can benefit patients suffering from hypertension and from symptoms of abnormally high cholesterol and triglycerides in the blood.

Favorable results were achieved after administration of the food supplement containing the yucca steroid saponin in tablet form, according to Dr. Robert Bingham, an orthopedic surgeon, founder and director of the National Arthritis Medical Clinic, who also has an arthritis and orthopedic practice in Yorba Linda, California.

Since Dr. Bingham's first report in 1975 called attention to the efficacy of yucca in treating arthritis, other physicians in Southwestern states and elsewhere have included yucca extract tablets in their regimen of treatment for arthritic disease. Their independent findings confirm Dr. Bingham's original conclusion that yucca extract is beneficial in treating these widespread diseases. Dr. Bingham's newest report on the effects of yucca upon high blood pressure and other health problems has been greeted with great interest and continues to be the subject of further clinical trials.

Results Of The Study

In the patient population, 64.6 percent were female and 34.5 percent were male. Osteoarthritis accounted for 58.9 percent of cases and rheumatoid arthritis for 41.1 percent. The disease had been present from two months to 42 years, with an average of 14.6 years.

The food supplement tablets were taken before, during and after meals—two tablets, three times a day—with no problems reported. The yucca concentrate proved to be non-irritating to the gastrointestinal tract. Some patients reported less gas and constipation.

Improvement in arthritis. Forty-nine percent felt less pain, stiffness, and swelling, the three major complaints of arthritis. This suggests that the normal intestinal flora of beneficial microscopic plant life may indeed be under stress in arthritis patients. The study concludes that yucca extract benefits normal bacterial forms in the alimentary canal.

Researchers considered it important that "no allergic manifestations appeared." This was not surprising, since yucca has served as a food for thousands of years. This seems to confirm evidence that the active principal, yucca saponin, is not absorbed into the blood but works within the small and large intestines. Its benefits are in the improvement and protection of intestinal flora rather than any direct action upon the arthritis.

There is strong evidence that some forms of arthritis may be caused or worsened by toxic substances in the intestines and that these toxins may be absorbed by the body. Most patients who report a reduction of swelling and stiffness in their joints are patients who suffer gastrointestinal disturbances associated with arthritis.

Yucca pills seem to inhibit pathological bacteria and protozoa that occur in the intestines. They also seem to help the natural and normal forms of bacteria found in the tract. Since there is very little or no absorption into the body, a patient does not need to worry about drug reactions or a conflict between yucca and other medications.

Since the publication of his original report, Dr. Bingham has continued to use yucca as a food supplement in the treatment of about 2,000 arthritis patients. Other physicians have added the yucca extract to their treatment regimens. Impressive results have been reported by Dr. Paul Isaacson of Tucson, Arizona, and Dr. Robert A. Elliott of Woodland Hills, California.

Dr. Isaacson reports that "the treatments are relieving the patient's discomfort and sometimes the swelling. I would say that 90 percent of my patients have gotten relief to some degree...before using yucca I just didn't get the results I'm getting now."

Dr. Elliott says that "about 50 percent of my patients have gained some relief from arthritis symptoms while taking the yucca tablets," and he noted that "yucca therapy seems to have a role in reducing cholesterol and triglyceride levels in the blood."

Details Of The 1978 Study

Dr. Bingham's 1975 report first noted that use of yucca in treating arthritis resulted in several unexpected side-effects—lowering of blood pressure, relief from headaches, reduction of blood cholesterol levels, and reduction of blood triglyceride levels. Additional studies appeared to be in order. Accordingly, 212 patients with high blood pressure and high cholesterol levels were given either yucca extract tablets or a placebo tablet in a random selection double-blind study: 124 patients suffered from osteoarthritis, and 88 had rheumatoid arthritis.

Each patient received a complete orthopedic examination, blood count, blood chemistry, and sedimentation rate tests. All patients were placed on high-protein diets stressing natural foods and vitamin supplements. They participated in exercise and physical therapy programs. During the study, all of the patients showed some improvement.

A random selection was used, neither the doctor nor patient knowing which tablet was given. Office nurses were the only ones who knew which patients received the placebo. The information was kept confidential until completion of the study. All patients were informed that the first tablets they would receive might be placebos or might be yucca tablets.

They were also told that if they were given the placebo, their treatment would be changed to the yucca tablets.

Results Of The Test

As in the original study, the medical team again found that about two-thirds of the patients received some benefit from taking yucca extract. None had any unpleasant reactions, complications, or ill effects from using yucca.

The 212 patients participating in the study were divided into three groups. The first group of 36 patients received the placebo tablets only. These were identical in appearance, color, size, and taste to the yucca tablets, but contained none of the yucca extract. A second group of 138 patients received only the yucca tablets. A third group of 38 patients was given the placebo for one or two months, then received yucca tablets for one to six months, or more. The average patient took the yucca tablets, or a liquid extract of equivalent potency, for six months to a year.

Results. Blood pressures were reduced, on the average, 13 mm/Hq in the placebo groups (who were on diet and exercise therapy); 24 mm/Hq in the yucca treated group. Blood cholesterol was reduced 40 mg/100 ml in the placebo groups; 110 mg/ba ml in the yucca group. Triglycerides were reduced 17 mg/100 ml in the placebo groups; 24 mg/lOG ml in the yucca group.

Dr. Bingham's report on these three factors show the results from the yucca treatment were greater than the reductions with placebos, diet, and exercises.

Dr. Bingham also suggests that yucca saponin may tend to break down the high molecular fats in foods whose absorption contributes to high blood pressure, hardening of the arteries, hypertriglyceridemia, and hypercholesterolemia.

One of the doctor's most significant findings was that no patient on yucca extract for six months or more continued to show an abnormally high blood pressure or excessive blood triglyceride and cholesterol levels. In other words, there were permanent benefits from the period of yucca therapy.

Certainly, the wild desert cactus plant known as the yucca is a natural benefactor to mankind.

Prevention And Treatment Of Arthritis

"Yucca plant saponin in the management of Arthritis." This food supplement, extracted from the desert yucca plant, has now been used in over 2,000 cases. It is a plant steroid substance, not absorbed in the intestines, which has a beneficial effect, helping to eliminate pathogenic organisms and plant forms, and reduce intestinal symptoms and disorders which are present in so many patients with arthritis. Besides less stiffness and soreness in the joints, which was the most frequent benefit of the treatment, many patients experience a relief of constipation, intermittent diarrhea, cramping, abdominal pains, intestinal gas, a lessening of headaches of the migraine type, and the blood picture of these patients showed a lowering of abnormal cholesterol levels.

IN SUMMARY: Newer treatment methods include the use of yucca as a food supplement, arthritis vaccines to improve the patient's immunity to infections, and anti-protozoal drugs should be given to patients with acute and active rheumatoid arthritis. Surgical replacement of joints destroyed by arthritis is safer and more successful after the patient has been on this type of medical and nutritional management for a month or more. The approach of Dr. Wayburn Mason to the treatment of rheumatoid arthritis, for the first time in medical history, makes improvement and the arrest of this disease a predictable result. The use of mega-vitamin therapy and minerals, particularly vitamin A, D, calcium, are essential to rebuilding of the bone and joint structures in arthritis patients. Further progress in the treatment of all forms of arthritis and prevention of most arthritic diseases are based on applied nutrition, exercise and careful medical management.

Bibliography

1. Bingham, Robert-*"Nutrition in the Treatment of Arthritis,"* Journal of Applied Nutrition, Vol. 25, pg. 112-125, Winter, 1972.

2. Bingham, Robert; Bellew, Bernard A.; and Bellew, Joeva G., "*Yucca Plant Saponin in the Management of Arthritis.*" Journal of Applied Nutrition, Vol. 27, No. 2 & 3, pg. 45-50. Fall, 1975.

3. Bingham, Robert"—*Rheumatoid Disease. Has One Investigator Found its Cause and Cure?*" The work of Dr. Roger Wayburn-Mason, Modern Medicine, pg. 3847, February 15, 1976.

Notes

CHAPTER 8

FLUORIDE AND THE GOVERNMENT LAWSUIT

In the latter part of 1983, an elderly lady living in Scotland found fluoride in her city drinking water. She was so upset that she took the Scottish government to court for putting poison in the water, and she won.

It is well to note that fluoride is against the law in many countries because it is a health hazard. It has also never been proven that fluoride reduces cavities. As one doctor said, after visiting the United States: "Even if fluoride did reduce cavities, who would want a full set of teeth long after you have died of cancer."

Fluoride is such a big business in America, they have even got the dentists washing mouths out with it. It's called double exposure now. You know, the dentist keeps telling you that his x-ray machine is too weak to give you cancer, so now they have added fluoride to their treatment, something just as dangerous.

With constant advertising for fluoride toothpaste, and fluoride also in all of our drinking water, it's no wonder that people from other countries shudder at the dangerous life we are living.

One Englishman told me that he can remember when it was the Mexican water that was not safe to drink, now the joke is to tell people planning to visit America, "It's a great place, but don't drink the water."

Fortunately, many groups of knowledgeable people have started demonstrating about this great threat to human life, and they also need your support. Don't let anyone say it's just in minute quantities, because you are already getting minute quantities of about 2,000 things each day that are dangerous and they do add up.

I understand that there are two brands of toothpaste on the market without fluoride. They are McLean's and Pepsodent. If you want to survive the drinking water problem, you need a reverse osmosis machine, not a filter or bottled water, which are sometimes worse.

Purest Water Available

Pure water is the greatest necessity for all forms of life, and yet today it is almost impossible to obtain. The additives used by the water departments are doing us almost as much damage as would the untouched polluted water.

Water distillers are great, but expensive. Reverse osmosis, I feel, is the answer, as it takes no machine to operate and no electrical power. The reverse osmosis water purifier costs less than half of the regular water distiller. Reverse osmosis developed by the U.S. Department of Interior License #3417870 is the finest home water purification process available. Purwater systems typically removes 95 percent of total dissolved solids plus all bacteria, pesticides, asbestos, radiation, organics, dissolved gasses, virus, turbidity, discoloration, amoebae, custs, spores, and reduces suspected cancer-causing organic chemicals, like trihalomethanes (THMs), carbon tetrachloride, benzene, PCBs to safe levels.

How does this marvelous system work? Polluted water is forced by water pressure against a semipermeable membrane. Purified water molecules easily pass through the membrane, while pollutants cannot pass through and are washed down the drain.

CHAPTER 9
ILLNESSES AND DISEASES

There are many benefits from a good exercise program, and some of them are a reduction of fatigue, more energy, better thinking, improved circulation and lowering of high blood pressure in many instances. It dispels despair and anxiety, and we feel sure, helps the body fight off such things as heart troubles and cancer. The exercise program must be used in conjunction with a good diet of at least 50 percent live food, such as fruit, vegetables and nuts.

You do not need to enter into a heavy exercise program, but rather something that you can stay with for life, something that you feel comfortable with. I lift free weights each day, cycle three miles, do sit-ups and end up each morning with a sauna and ice cold plunge in the special plunge tank. Then I feet ready to tackle the world. I do this after drinking one pint of lemon juice at room temperature.

Regular exercise changes the metabolism of your body, lowering body fats such as lipoprotein cholesterol which, if allowed to build up, predisposes you to all kinds of artery and heart troubles. It also possibly helps prevent the accumulation of fats in the arteries.

I believe that you must combine exercise and diet. If you just diet alone then your metabolism slows down also, so you burn fewer calories and so have a harder time losing weight than if you were eating normally but exercising considerably. Vigorous exercise will offset the slowdown of your metabolism and will hasten the weight loss without making you feel depressed. Did you know that mild exercise actually reduces your appetite?

Because muscle weighs more than fat, it is quite possible that you may not lose pounds, but will lose many inches. Do not worry about the weight as you are just "redistributing" your body, and turning fat into muscle. People will remark that you must have lost 30 lbs. when actually it was only 10 lbs, but that was fluid that makes you look old and bloated in all the wrong places

Isometric Exercises: Pushing and straining your muscles against immovable objects. The best exercises in the world are isometric. You can do them anywhere, and you don't need to buy expensive equipment. Set aside 20 minutes each day, except Sunday, and do sit-ups, push-ups, leg lifts-then lean against the wall and push with your back, as though you are pushing a car. Now push the wall with your hands (facing the wall). You must exert yourself but don't overdo it, just try to do a little bit better each week. The results will astound you. Try to walk at least one and a half miles a day.

Health spas and gymnasiums make their money out of the "spur-of-the-moment" people who suddenly have the urge to better themselves so they buy a lifetime membership in a club, go just two or three times, then never return. If every member showed up at the same time, the place would not be able to hold a tenth of them, in most cases.

Also, many homes have closets full of exercise equipment purchased, once again, on the spur of the moment and rarely, if ever, used. That is why it is better to return once again to the simple way of exercising, as outlined above. After all, you already own a wall, so why bother with anything else.

Before you start any exercise program, stretch your body, like a cat does upon waking. You have to get flexibility into your muscles before you start. A cat never wakes up and starts dashing around as we do when our alarm sounds in the morning. He lays and stretches his legs, back and neck and this is what we should also do prior to getting out of bed. You can set your alarm for five minutes earlier, and that will give you enough time to make yourself supple and flexible.

ALCOHOLISM

When a person is healing people but is not a medical doctor, does not belong to the A.M.A. and if he is not prescribing harmful drugs, then be can expect to be persecuted.

So it was with some concern that the staff of one clinic was shaken when the stranger standing bleary-eyed in the middle of the waiting room said, “I have a very responsible position and need help.”

Dr. Oswald saw him at once and soon found out that the man was an alcoholic to the extent he was about to lose everything, career, home and family.

Quite used to helping friends and enemies alike, Dr. Oswald told him, "The only way for an alcoholic to be cured is for him to want to be cured.” The man said that he wanted to be free of this thing that was destroying his life, more than anything else in the world, so Oswald started him on the following program.

First came the colon cleanse mentioned earlier, and so important as the first step in any recovery. Next came the phosphates that fed the man’s nervous system constantly. Then the correcting of the chronic imbalances created by the alcohol. Once this step is completed then all craving for alcohol disappears. The patient is then taken off all sugar and sugar-based foods. And special liver rebuilding tablets are administered.

In this man’s case, the treatment only took two weeks to become totally effective, but Dr. Oswald emphasizes the point that during this time the person must be worked with very closely. It is not as effective if a person is just sent home with the information in order to do it all himself. He needs the encouragement and help of a trained person on a 24-hour basis. When I took up this point with Hanne Kramb, she said her therapy was the same except that she had found certain pressure points on the ear that allows the patient to take quicker advantage of the therapy.

Mr. Rolf Effern, Hanne’s pharmacist and licensed chemist, told us of a certain herb now available that prohibits an alcoholic from drinking, for each time he does he becomes very sick to the stomach. The difficulty, of course, is getting the patient to take the herbal formula each day.

SERGEANT BORKOWSKI AND ATHLETE'S FOOT

In Poland, the enlisted men suffered terribly from athlete's foot, which is highly contagious. This uncomfortable scourge spread through the camps like the plague.

Sergeant Borkowski came from the town of Lodz, 100 miles from Warsaw, and upon reviewing his service record with a view to promotion, the group of examining officers found that the Sergeant had never suffered from any foot ailment during his 17 years of service, not even the very common athlete's foot.

This discovery caused great excitement for if the man had a secret remedy or preventative for this, it would be worth a fortune, plus it would be of great benefit to the whole army.

It was with great embarrassment that Borkowski stood in the health officer's board room and, in front of seven other officers, was forced to explain exactly what he did to avoid foot problems.

It was simply that each morning, while taking a shower, Borkowski urinated on his feet, just as his old father had told him to do. There was certainly no glamor here and no money to be made, but the information was officially passed around to others. It seems, upon careful study, that urine has thousands of antibodies that are most effective in fighting infections.

It was with enormous embarrassment to the Canadian Television Network when they interviewed a high Indian official from New Delhi on live television, seen by hundreds of thousands of viewers, the announcer, a very proper individual, asked the Indian to what he credited his good health and excellent skin to which he quickly replied, "I drink my own urine." I suppose that it would be hard to gain your composure after an answer like that. He was not joking, of course. Many investigations have been done pertaining to mare's urine as it seems to give the immune system a giant boost, but somehow I don't think the Western world will ever accept that. I can imagine the look on a bleary-eyed patient's face when he looks up at you from his bed and says, "What is this stuff I'm drinking, anyway?" And you tell him!!

Colds, Catarrh And The Roman Army

Before going on long marches or into battle, the Roman army was fed a small amount of garlic each day. This would ward off colds, plus give the soldiers strength and stamina. The gladiators were fed massive steaks, done very rare, along with garlic cloves. The meat was to bring out their anger and ferocity in the arena and the garlic would give them strength and cause the fight to last much longer.

Down through the centuries garlic has been well known as a quick remedy for colds and catarrh. In many countries it is used as a necklace worn by people with sore throats or bad head or chest conditions. The strange thing is that if someone wears a garlic necklace and they have a sore throat, the strength of the garlic quickly diminishes. But if you wear one and are healthy, then the garlic retains its strength for many days. Chewing a small piece of garlic purifies the teeth, gums, tongue and throat, rids the intestines of parasites and mucus, right down to the colon.

It is peculiar that we pull away from someone who has just eaten garlic, which should be a sign to us that they have just purified their body, yet we gladly hug and kiss someone who has just finished a hamburger and milk shake, loading their intestines with thick green putrid mucus. If you live in a cold damp climate, then to avoid colds, bronchitis, asthma and sore throats just crush up two vitamin C tablets (1,000 mg), mix it with hot water and let it trickle down your throat. Follow with a garlic piece and you can breathe better right away. Very unscientific, but as long as it works, what does it matter.

Dysentery And The British Officer

When the British army was fighting the Dervishes and the Fuzzy Wuzzies in Africa, the most common complaint among the solders and officers alike was stomach problems, due to the drastic change of water, diet and weather. The same thing happened to the soldiers serving in the Khyber Pass area of India. After exhausting large supplies of medicine that did not work, a captain in the medical corps found that if you placed one ounce of port wine and one ounce of brandy into a glass and sipped on it, then repeated the procedure every three hours, the problem would disappear in every case.

The trouble with this, however, was that when the regular soldiers learned about this treatment, there soon appeared a lineup outside the dispensary, with all the men claiming upset stomachs.

I have learned from visiting friends in Acapulco that it is also very effective against Montezuma's revenge.

Gallstones

Many people I have spoken to have gall stones on top of their other problems. Here is what a top American nutritionist told me to do about this, simply and easily without surgery.

My whole family has done this successfully.

Drink one quart of apple juice daily for five days. This will soften up the stones to such an extent that you could squash them in your fingers.

On the sixth day, skip dinner and, at 6 p.m., take a tablespoonful of Epsom salts with water. Repeat at 8 p.m. At 10 p.m. make a cocktail of four ounces of olive oil and four ounces of fresh-squeezed lemon juice. Shake vigorously and drink right down. In the morning, you will pass green stones varying from the size of grains of sand to some as large as your thumb nail. You won't feel a thing, but will be amazed at the results. Thousands have done this instead of major surgery.

THE KIDNEYS

When it comes to taking good care of the kidneys, I found it very strange that people from over 30 countries that I visited all had the same old ancient remedy. They claim this simple remedy was passed down to them by their forefathers who always knew just what to do with any kidney problem.

As we have discussed, your body can heal itself, providing you give it a chance, so the first thing you have to do to help the kidneys is simply to "flush them out." Once this is done to mother nature's satisfaction, then the healing is very quick.

Each morning squeeze one whole lemon into a pint of warm water (distilled if possible) and drink it down. It goes straight to the kidneys and starts its purifying and healing. No sugar allowed.

Apart from this, what a wonderful way to start the day, with a good old-fashioned vitamin health drink instead of that terrible coffee that aids in screwing up the kidneys.

TENSION CAN MAKE YOU ILL

Cancer Help Center

In the history of mankind, there may never have been a time when individuals were free from the challenging circumstances that life presents in some form or other. Today, we are certainly conscious of tremendous pressures which seem to assail us from all directions and which so often contribute to tension both in body and mind.

During stressful conditions, the normal reaction of the body is to pour hormones, such as cortisone and adrenaline, into the blood stream, thus increasing blood pressure, heart rate and breath intake and preparing us for fight or flight. Obviously, this is highly necessary in the appropriate circumstances, but unfortunately we can become unconsciously locked in this condition, even though facing far less demanding situations. For example, pressures from personal relationships, financial worries, fears of redundancy, bottled-up resentment, frustration, niggling anxieties and fears, one or all can add fuel to the Flight-Fight Response so that we rarely switch off, if at all. The body is consequently forced to produce steroids which can interfere with our protective immune system and the increase in metabolism produced by stress may well use up valuable energy needed for the maintenance of health. All of us produce many thousands of cancer cells daily; under normal conditions, these are efficiently dealt with by the immune system. If the latter becomes impaired, however, the cancer cells may get out of hand. It also follows, of course, that an impaired immune system lays our bodies open to other diseases as well, so it is in the interest of our own present and future well-being that we learn to recognize a condition of stress in ourselves which has gotten out of hand. We then learn to relax into a restful state in which the blood pressure and heart rate drops and the body can recharge, revitalize and resuscitate its immune system. Besides, this is a delightful state and should be seen to be as nourishing for the body as good food and proper breathing. Lack of attention to the fundamental needs of the body may cause more disease than tension itself.

Everyone Should Learn To Relax

Apart from being an effective way of coping positively with stress and the disorders it causes, relaxation helps us to avoid unnecessary fatigue and to recover from it more quickly. It gives the body's own natural healing rhythms a chance to function more efficiently. It can raise the threshold of tolerance to pain. It aids personal relationships which can be such a cause of tension because it is easier to get on with people when you are relaxed and at ease. It also helps us to sleep better and enhances our feeling of well- being.

“Dis-ease”: An Inner State

Through relaxation the body is able to resolve the physical tension which can arise from the day-to-day challenges of living. The real causes of tension, however, lie within ourselves and cannot really be blamed on others. It is our inability to come to terms with situations and conditions in ourselves that leads us to a state of resistance, be it of a forceful nature, or one of apathy. The mind will contrive most wonderfully to justify our own negative attitudes and actions, including the stands we take in our relationships with others. Relaxation of the body alone will not resolve these inner conflicts. We will need to go deeper into the process of training the mind to become positive and one-pointed in bringing about a state of well-being within ourselves.

Meditation

This leads us to meditation. There are many forms of meditation, but our main motivation in meditating is to heal ourselves in whatever way is appropriate.

In seeking true health, we may need to understand the relationship between body, mind and spirit and it is important to realize what power the mind has in directing thoughts either creatively or destructively. And energy follows thought. The mind can be likened to a conductor of an orchestra. The orchestra can be conducted so that each member gives of his or her best and harmony results, or there can be a lack of coordination and discord. If the latter arises in the orchestra of our bodily, emotional, mental and spiritual needs, then we experience dis-ease in some form. It is our responsibility to see that our own mind directs its thoughts positively toward the well-being of the whole.

First of all, let us be quite dear, meditation is not an opting out of life. Rather, it enables us to live life more fully—more usefully and more creatively. It enables us to enrich the relationship of body, mind and spirit, through which true healing flows.

The first thing we need to achieve is relaxation. We cannot meditate if we are not relaxed, although we can be relaxed and not meditating. Deepening degrees of relaxation can lead us naturally toward meditation. These are stages on the way. The mind, however, has to be encouraged to become one pointed, alert and poised. It has to be trained to cease from showering us with uninvited thoughts, such as items for the shopping list, or the state of our bank balance! The required state might be likened to a sentry on duty on a moonless night: Body relaxed and composed, but senses alert for the slightest indication of noise of an intruder. There is no question of going to sleep'.

A Daily Routine

Initially, we could say reaching a meditative state involves four things; we could call them "Four Quiet States." When our health is involved, it is important to try and set aside three periods of relaxation/meditation of 10 to 20 minutes each and every day. It is only as difficult as you yourself make it, though young children add an extra challenge! You can spend 10 or 20 minutes when you awake and again before you go to sleep at night. To begin with, the mind finds all sorts of excuses but it responds to firmness, kindness and a sense of humor!

The Four Quiet States

I ***A Quiet Environment***—A place where you feel "at ease," free from door bells, or telephone. This is your special time. There is no need to feel in the least guilty in allowing time to revitalize your body and to link with your innermost resources.

2. ***A Quiet Body***—This means a relaxed body in a comfortable position with a straight spine. Whatever position you adopt, be it lying, sitting, kneeling, or full lotus, if you are too cozy, you run the risk of falling asleep. If so, the relax-

ation you achieve will be from the body only and even then the body does not necessarily relax fully in sleep. The deepest relaxation is attained when the mind is involved also.

3. ***A Quiet Receptive Attitude***—Perhaps most important of all. Don't strive for goals, don't expect anything, rather ALLOW relaxation to happen. Allow the breath to deepen in the abdomen, not in the upper chest. The deepening of the breath in the abdominal region has a steadying, calming effect and draws us into deeper relaxation.

4. **A *Quiet Mind***—"Quiet" in the context of being "unbusy," but alert and poised. This may require the repetition of a special word, or mantra to keep the mind focused; quietly concentrating on the ebb and flow of the breath is another method; using a symbol or image which evokes a state of well-being, or the innermost source of all true healing, is yet another.

Whatever method proves most appropriate for us is what matters, thereafter meditation can help us reactivate our powers of healing and find an inner peace which enables us to enjoy life more fully.

Cream Of Cathay

Miracles Still Happen!

The man walked into the Las Vegas Gym and he was beaming with good reason. The skin cancer that had plagued him for many years had gone completely in three days. He estimated a cost of $2,000 spent with dermatologists and other experts all to no avail. Yet, just by a crazy fluke, he had rid himself of this disease in three days at no cost at all.

He was the fourth person to discover the solution in the past two weeks, so most of us were getting used to hearing about it.

They had all simply discovered what the Indians of South

America had known for the past 6,000 years. They would boil the bark of a very special tree that grows in their rain forest and spread the solution on their faces and bodies. The Vikings who visited them in those far-off days often took home boat loads of the bark which proved even more valuable than gold.

Strangely enough, medical science in America has recently found that this bark contains a very powerful antibiotic.

At the same time the Vikings were visiting South America, the Chinese at the ancient city of Xian were treating all skin problems with an herbal solution which was quite powerful. It seldom failed to get results. In America, seven American and Chinese doctors worked together investigating this herb, along with others. They chose to call it the FU-ZHENG therapy and they proved to everyone's satisfaction that these herbs are most powerful. "American Cancer Society 0008-543-83/0701/0070."

Can you imagine the results if these two products mentioned above were combined into a smooth, cool, healing cream?

We did this last year in London, then a scientist came to us with the natural fragrance of rose water, in use before the birth of Christ. Cleopatra would bathe in rose water each day. The petals, gathered by virgins dressed in long, white robes would only be picked by the light of the moon. Rose water was also the most popular fragrance during the life of Christ.

Jason Winters was the first person to mix these astonishing ingredients together into a thick, cooling, healing cream with the fragrance of roses on a summer evening.

This skin care cream has already attracted the attention of the cosmetic trade and also inquiries from the world's largest suntan lotion company who wish to make it the base for all cosmetics and oils.

Mr. Rolph, top cosmetic chemist, claims that Cream of Cathay is the ultimate beauty cream for softness, coolness and the look of vibrant health.

Heart Troubles And High Blood Pressure

A common remedy for heart troubles and high blood pressure is cayenne liquid. Within a few moments the blood pressure of most people is back to normal and all pain is gone.

Easily available in Australia and selling in massive quantities this natural, harmless "food" is almost impossible to obtain in America. From what we are led to believe, heart problems are the number one killer in North America so I leave it to the reader to draw his own conclusions as to why cayenne liquid is not available to everyone.

In Sydney, New South Wales, Australia, a man of 40 dropped down with extreme heart pains right in the middle of the street. An ambulance was called right away. A lady from a nearby house had watched what had taken place and calmly walked out and, leaning over the man, placed a pillow under his head. Then she spooned a little cayenne liquid into the man's mouth. Within three minutes the pains had stopped and the man got up and walked away. The policeman on the spot was flabbergasted, the ambulance men were very upset to learn that their patient had escaped them and there was talk of charging the helpful lady with practicing medicine without a license, but the case was dropped.

Have you ever seen a car accident in America where tow trucks, all listening to the police radio band, rush to the spot like vultures, each one trying desperately to hook onto one car or another to insure themselves $75 or more? Well, sometimes ambulance drivers remind me of the same thing. In Las Vegas one hospital guarantees that if you take an ambulance to their hospital and you have to check in, they will pay the ambulance fee. It's almost like paying a finder's fee for obtaining an investor in a company.

White Sugar And The Reproductive System

It wasn't until Peter Hill and his wife Jean moved onto the farm they had purchased that they noticed the ants. There were millions of them, not only in every room of the house, but all over the 10 acres they owned. The two children were bitten quite often and the bites were both painful and often infected. They tried spraying thoroughly, but after two days the ants were back. Then they called in professional exterminators but to no avail. The ants would disappear for two days, then start coming back worse than ever. The situation became intolerable when the children could not go out to play in the yard and Peter, working the land, would have fresh bites to contend with each night. They appealed to the "Letters to the Editor" of the local newspaper and many solutions came in from friends and neighbors, but nothing worked.

One day, however, when things looked their worst, a small booklet was sent to them through the mail. It was written in the Greek language and the sender had been concerned enough to write the English translation under each line The author said it was guaranteed to work. The solution was to purchase 500 lbs. of white refined sugar and pour little piles five inches high in every room of the house and in all covered areas of the land, such as in hollow logs, under boards and anywhere that the piles would not get wet.

In desperation they did exactly as described in the booklet. They had hundreds of little piles all over their land. In four months there was not an ant to be found and they have never returned. Now the reader may be excused for being skeptical, for I was also when I read the report. I thought that if you fed the ants, especially with delicious white sugar, the population would increase, not disappear entirely. But I had forgotten one thing. The sugar was delicious, but absolutely non-nutritious and highly toxic, which over three generations of ants (four months), broke down their health and destroyed their reproductive systems so they could not have young. This has since been proven in many laboratories. This is exactly what's happening to the human race but on a slower pace because our generations are many years, not weeks as are the ants.

HANNE KRAMB ON SEX

A 73-year-old man came to the clinic complaining that he had a 42-year-old wife but found that it was impossible for him to have sexual intercourse because of his age.

Hanne gave him acupuncture and injections of calves liver, pancreas and brain, along with Xian capsules. Within one month the man's wife called the clinic and asked Hanne Kramb if there was something she could give him to slow him down. Evidently it had worked too well. Sadly, nothing can be done for this man. One can only hope that his new-found vigor will cool as time goes by.

People visiting the Hanne Kramb clinic at Christmas time are astounded at what they find. Hundreds of gifts start arriving from grateful people all over the world, people who will never forget her and the help she gave them. I understand from one patient that the gifts fill up four complete rooms.

It seems as though God is using people like Hanne Kramb to spread love, health and happiness to those who have had all hope taken away from them by the so-called orthodox people.

The two products necessary for rejuvenation are Xian capsules and/or Solcosplen tablets, depending upon your condition.

The Miracle Lade Of Honzrath

A 72-year-old medical doctor arrived at the clinic on a stretcher. He had been to see all his medical friends in a desperate bid for help but they could not help him. They had all told him to go home and prepare to die. He was, in fact, a hopeless case

Told constantly that he was, after all, 72 years old and could expect problems like this, he finally gathered enough strength to sign himself out of the hospital and, as a last resort, had the ambulance people take him to the Hanne Kramb clinic. Told by his medical doctors to take three tablets each day for his Parkinson's disease he did, and the day he signed himself out of the hospital, take 10 of them. His shaking was so very bad that it was almost impossible to work on him.

That man three months later is back at work, running his own practice again with no shaking and no illness of any kind. The doctor's family has stated publicly that they would never seek help from anyone other than Hanne Kramb again. I arrived in Luxembourg on April 4, 1984 to be interviewed by a large magazine and also local newspapers. It was then that I started hearing these remarkable stories everywhere I turned. I decided that I must visit this clinic myself and arrived just a few days later. It was an hour's drive from the Luxembourg airport across the border into West Germany. The clinic was located in the beautiful town of Honzrath and was situated on the top of a tree-studded hill.

The atmosphere was just like home with everyone so friendly and kind. Hanne Kramb had used my Tribalene in her practice for a long time and that certainly was a pleasant surprise to me.

I at once issued her the challenge, "What's the matter with me?" purposely while the media was still there doing my interview. She asked me to look into the end of a magnifying glass while she looked into the other end in order to study my left eye. At once she said that I had kidney damage and a backbone out of alignment, especially in my neck.

She was right on both counts. Years before I had suffered kidney damage while playing soccer and also, because I "headed" the ball so much, I had injured my neck muscles. Doctors had told me this for years after expensive tests and many questions, yet this lady knew it at once with no questions at all.

The news media took photos of her treating me with acupuncture and a neck adjustment which took 15 minutes to correct both situations. She also took another five minutes to correct my constantly draining sinuses. The effect was immediate. She simply opened up the blocked nerves that were causing the problem and at once the drainage took place in my nose instead of the back of my throat.

Notes

Chapter 10

Death Begins In The Colon

Important Discussion Of Alimentary Toxemia Before The Royal Society Of Medicine Of Great Britain

Recently the subject of alimentary toxemia was discussed in London before the Royal Society of Medicine by 57 of the leading physicians of Great Britain. Among the speakers were eminent surgeons, physicians, and specialists in the various branches of medicine.

Poisons Of Alimentary Intestinal Toxemia

The following is a list of the various poisons noted by several speakers: Indol, phenol, cresol, indican, sulphurretted hydrogen, ammonia, histidine, urobilin, methylmercaptan, tetramerhylendiamin, pentamethy lendiamine, putrescine, cadaverine, neurin, choline, muscarine, butyric acid, bera-imidazzolethylamine, methylgandinine, ptomarropine, botulin, tyramine, agmatine, tryptophane, sepsin, idolethylamine, sulpher-roglobine.

Of the 36 poisons mentioned above, several are highly active, producing the most profound effects and in very small quantities. In cases of alimentary toxemia some one or several of these poisons is constantly bathing the delicate body cells and setting up charges which finally result in grave disease.

Symptoms And Diseases Due To Alimentary Toxemia

It should be understood that these findings are not mere theories but are the results of demonstrations in actual practice by eminent physicians. Of course it is not claimed that alimentary toxemia is the only cause of all the symptoms and diseases named. Although of many it may be the sole or principal cause, some of them are due to other causes as well. In the following summary the various symptoms and disorders mentioned in the discussion in London, to which reference has been made above, are grouped and classified.

The Digestive Organs

Duodenal ulcer causing partial or complete obstruction of the duodenum, pyloric spasm, pyloric obstruction, distention and dilation of the stomach, gastric ulcer, cancer of the stomach, adhesions of the omentum to the stomach and liver, inflammation of the liver, cancer of the liver.

The muscular wall of the intestine, as well as other muscles, atrophy so that the passage of their contents is hindered. The abdominal visceral lose their normal relationship to the spine and to each other on account of weakening of the abdominal muscles. These displacements are much more marked and serious in women. Other conditions are: Catarrh of the intestines, foul gases and foul smelling stools, colitis, acute enteritis, appendicitis, acute and chronic; adhesions and "kinks" of the intestines, visceroptosis, enlargement of spleen, distended abdomen, tenderness of the abdomen, summer diarrhea of children, inflammation of pancreas, chronic dragging abdominal pains, gastritis, cancer of pancreas, inflammatory changes of gall bladder, cancer of gall bladder, gallstones, degeneration of liver, cirrhosis of liver, infection of the gums and decay of the teeth, ulcers in the mouth and pharynx.

Heart And Blood Vessels

Wasting and weakening of the heart muscles, microbic cyanosis from breaking up of blood cells, fatty degeneration of the heart, endocarditis, myocarditis, subnormal blood pressure, enlargement of the heart, the dilation of the aorta, high blood pressure, arteriosclerosis, permanent dilation of arteries.

Dr. W. Bezley says: "There are a few phases of cardiovascular trouble (disease of heart and blood vessels) with which disorder of some part of the alimentary tract is not causatively associated."

The Nervous System

Headaches of various kinds—frontal, occipital, temporal, dull or intense, hemicrania, headache of a character to lead to a mistaken diagnosis of brain tumor Dr. Lane tells of a case where a surgeon had proposed an operation for the removal of a tumor from the frontal lobe of the brain. The difficulty was wholly removed by the exclusion of the colon. Acute neuralgia pains in the legs, neuritis, twitching of the eyes and of muscles of face, arms, legs, etc. Lassitude, irritability, disturbances of the nervous system, varying from simple headaches to absolute collapse, mental and physical depression. Insomnia, troubled sleep, unpleasant dreams, unrefreshing sleep, the patient awakening tired, excessive sleepiness, patient falling asleep in the daytime, shivery sensation across lower spinal region, burning sensations in face, hands, etc., epileptiform tic, typhoid state, paralysis, chronic fatigue, horror of noises, morbid introspection, perverted moral feelings, melancholia, mania, loss of memory, difficulty of mental concentration, imbecility, insanity, delirium, coma.

The Eyes

Degenerative changes in the eye, inflammation of the lens, inflammation of the optic nerve, hardening of the lens, sclerotitis, sclerokeratitis, iritis, iridocyclitis, cataract, recurrent hemorrhage in the retina, eye dull and heavy.

The Skin

Formation of wrinkles, thin, inelastic, starch skin; pigmentations of the skin—yellow, brown, slate-black, blue; muddy complexion, offensive secretion from the skin of flexures, thickening of the skin of the back of the skin—sores and boils, pemphigus, pruritus, herpes, eczema, dermatitis, lupus erythematosus, acne rosacea, cold, clammy extremities; dark circles under the eyes, seborrhea, psoriasis, pityriasis, alopecia, lichen, planus, jaundice, "An infinitesimal amount of poison may suffice to cause skin eruption."

Muscles And Joints

Degeneration of the muscles, "Muscles waste and become soft and in advanced cases tear easily. In young life the muscular debility produces the deformities which are called dorsal excurvation or round shoulders, lateral curvature, flat feet and knock knees." Weakness of abdominal muscles causes accumulation of feces in the pelvic colon which renders evacuation of contents more and more difficult. Prominence of bones, rheumatic pains simulating sciatica and lumbago, various muscular pains, muscular rheumatism, arthritis deformities, synovitis, rickets, arthritis, acute and chronic. Tubercle and rheumatoid arthritis are the direct result of intestinal intoxication. Dr. Lane says, "I do not believe it is possible for either of these diseases to obtain a foothold except in the presence of stasis."

Genito-Urinary And Reproductive Organs

Various displacements, distortion and disease of the uterus, change in the whole forms contour of woman, fibrosis of breast, wasting of breasts, induration of breasts, subacute and chronic mastitis, cancer of breast, metritis and endometritis, frequent urination, albumosuria, acute nephritis, moveable kidney, floating kidney. Dr. Lanes goes so far as to say, "Autointoxication plays so large a part in the development of disease of the female genitourinary apparatus that they may be regarded by the gynecologist as a product of intestinal stasis."

General Disorders And Disturbances Of Nutrition

Degeneration of the organs of elimination, especially the liver, kidneys (Bright's disease), and spleen, pernicious anemia, lowered resistance to infection of all kind, premature senile decay, retardation of growth in children, accompanied by mental irritability and muscular fatigue, adenoids, enlarged tonsils, scurvy, enlarged thyroid (goitre), various tumors and Raynaud's disease. In those who apparently suffer no harm from constipation during a long series of years there is perhaps, as suggested by Hertz, a partial immunity established. The writer has long believed that such an immunity is sometimes established in the very obstinate constipation which accompanies absolute fasting because of the cleansing of the tongue and reappearance of appetite which often occurs at the end of the second or third week of the fast, a phenomenon very like that which appears in typhoid fever and other continued fevers. It must not be supposed, however, that even the establishment of so-called immunity insures the body against all injury. The labor of eliminating an enormous amount of virulent toxins, which fails upon the kidneys, damages the renal tissues and produces premature failure of these essential organs. Any process which develops toxins within the body is a menace to the life of the tissues and should be suppressed as far as possible and as quickly as possible.

The fact that symptoms of poisoning resulting from constipation do not appear at once is no evidence that injury is not done. Dr. William Hunter, in the course of the London discussion, remarked that the fact that chronic constipation "might exist in certain individuals as an almost permanent condition without apparently causing ill health is due solely to the power and protective action of the liver. It is not any evidence of the comparative harmlessness of constipation per se, but only an evidence that some individuals possess the cecum and the colon of an ox, with the liver of a pig, capable of doing any amount of distoxification." In the face of such an array of evidence, backed up by authority of nearly 60 eminent English physicians-and many hundreds of other English, U.S., German and French physicians whose names might be added—it is no longer possible to ignore the importance of alimentary toxemia or autointoxication as a fact in the production of disease. To no other single cause is it possible to attribute one-tenth as many various and widely diverse disorders. "It may be said that almost every chronic disease known is directly or indirectly due to the influence of bacterial poisons absorbed from the intestine. The colon may be justly looked upon as a veritable Pandora's box, out of which come more human misery and suffering, mental and moral, as well as physical, than from any other source."

The colon is a sewage system, but by neglect and abuse it becomes a cesspool. When it is clean and normal we are well and happy. Let it stagnate and it will distill the poisons of decay, fermentation and putrefaction into the blood, poisoning the brain and nervous system so that we become mentally depressed and irritable. It will poison the heart so that we are weak and listless, poison the lungs so that the breath is foul, poison the digestive organs so that we are distressed and bloated, and poison the blood so that the skin is sallow and unhealthy. In short, every organ of the body is poisoned and we age prematurely, look and feel old, the joints are stiff and painful, neuritis, dull eyes and a sluggish brain overtake us, the pleasure of living is gone.

The preceding information should impress you with the vital importance of bowel regularity to you and every member of your family.

Chapter 11
The Colon

When I decided to write about a complete cleanse for body, mind and spirit I fully knew the importance of the colon.

In my search for the right expert in the field of colon therapy the name Dr. Vanita Forsyth came up again and again. I located her in Kingman, Arizona, but only after I had found out the following:

During her life she had always suffered from bowel problems which resulted in the loss of her colon, long intestine, the rectum and part of the small intestine surgically.

When it was too late for her, she found the importance of a clean colon and regular bowel movements and so has devoted her whole life to helping others avoid the tragedy that she endured.

She is now an expert in her field and where others would have given up on life completely after such an operation, Dr. Forsyth had just started to live and to fight.

Thousands of people have benefited from her knowledge and people can only suspect what terrible illness and operations they would have had to endure had they not changed their way of life after talking to this lady.

Dr. Forsyth has been there. She has eaten wrongly, suffered the consequences of a horrible operation. What better person for America to turn to and, of course, people are by the thousands.

Following is an interview with this most remarkable, attractive lady.

Signs That You Need The Bowel Boutique

- If you are tired all the time.
- If you have to tip the bell boy to help you carry the bags under your eyes.

- If your abdomen hangs down over your belt.
- If your friends are planning a surprise baby shower for you and you're not pregnant.
- If your face is bloated.
- If your bowel movements smell so bad you can't stand to be in the same room with yourself. If your 24-hour deodorant surrenders in 24 minutes.
- If your wife won't kiss you anymore because of your foul breath and draining sinuses.
- If your eyes are so bloodshot you have to go to the blood bank to have them drained.
- If you weigh in on a public scale and the card comes back, "One at a time please."
- If you tell your husband every night, "Sorry, I have a headache," and you really do.
- If you pass wind in the office and your secretary passes out.
- If your eyelids hang down over your eyes so far you look like you're asleep.
- If when you take off your socks, the dog leaves the room.
- If your body odor would put a skunk to shame.
- If every time you belch it kicks on the air conditioner.

Do You Recommend Laxatives?

No, not as a routine thing. Do you realize there are more than 40,000 laxatives used in America today, so that should give you an idea what kind of shape the country is in.

I would recommend them only under certain circumstances. But not as a habit, unless there is no other way. The catch is, most people THINK there is no other way, that is why this bowel cleaning program may be the answer to their prayers. Laxatives are recommended when you begin the bowel cleaning program for the first three days only. One lady had to take laxatives for 25 years and is completely dependent on them. Her bowels will not move at all without six strong laxatives every night. I even recommended Dr.

Christopher's Nature-lax 2 which tones and strengthens, cleans and provides some laxative effect. It didn't help moving the bowel. Her bowel is damaged to the point, I fear, that she will never be able to do without laxatives. Even if laxatives were safe, they still wouldn't remove those deposits that have been building and hardening in you for years.

What Makes People Constipated?

There are two major reasons for this: One—when the food you eat is not ALL expelled within a day or two, this is constipation, whether you realize it or not. This leads to too long retention of feces, causing it to harden and dry out as too much moisture is reabsorbed from the colon, clogging and irritating the nerve endings in the bowel lining. Two—eating the wrong foods: a) a diet high in mucus-forming foods such as sugars, dairy products, meat, eggs, processed highly-refined foods, white flour, cooked foods and not enough raw. b) a diet low in fiber. High fibrous foods include raw fruits and vegetables, steamed or baked fruits and vegetables, whole grains, beans, peas, lentils, etc.) Not drinking enough plain, pure water.

Medications—antibiotics are famous for wiping out the good guys in the bowel (the favorable intestinal flora, leaving it wide open for the bad guys, such as harmful bacteria and virus to move in). According to Dr. John Harvey Kellogg the ratio should be about 85 percent acidophilus and 15 percent bacillus coli (bad guys). These bad guys thrive on undigested protein (mostly meat) and are gas producers. This ratio is usually reversed in most people and the bad guys outnumber the good guys 85 percent to 15 percent.

The Bible states, "Why do you take into your body that which your body has no need."

One autopsy revealed a colon to be nine inches in diameter with a passage through it no larger than a pencil! The rest was caked-up, layer upon layer, of encrusted fecal material. This accumulation can have the consistency of truck tire rubber. It's hard and black. Another autopsy revealed a stagnant colon to weigh in at an incredible 40 pounds! Imagine carrying around all that morbid accumulated waste.

When the bowel is dirty it can harbor an amazing variety of very harmful bacteria and parasites. It's interesting to note that worms outrank cancer as man's deadliest enemy on a worldwide basis! It is estimated that 200 million people are infected by these intestinal parasites.

These worms range in size from microscopic single-cell animals to two-foot-long tapeworms! These parasites kill more people annually than does cancer. One in four people in the world today are infected by roundworms. The U.S. is not immune to these parasites as the number of cases has increased in the past few years.

It is my opinion that more people than this have parasites. A lot of them have never been diagnosed properly. I might add it could be as high as 80 percent. I was one of them. It can happen to you.

What Size Should The Proper Stool Be?

"When your colon is healthy you will have two well-formed bowel movements a day. Every morning you'll have a huge movement which should altogether be two to four feet long. Later on in the day you'll have another movement which will be about one half the size of the first. These stools should be expelled effortlessly—within seconds after you sit down." V.E. Irons, Healthview Newsletter #10.

Obviously if the stools are long and the size of a pencil or look like rabbit pellets or if they are short and hard and if you pass mucus, blood or half-digested food, this is indicative of poor bowel function.

Should Normal Stool Be The Same Color?

Yes, the color should generally be about the same—brown. This may vary temporarily depending on what you eat, e.g., beets or spinach will affect the color but if it is grey or yellow, something is wrong.

Do Many People Suffer From A Poor Colon?

About 95 percent of the population. The other five percent has either been on a perfect diet since birth or live in the Himalayas.

It is estimated that over 75 million Americans suffer from bowel problems. The second leading cause of death in the cancer field is cancer of the bowel. More than 100,000 people a year die from colon cancer.

Colitis and diverticulitis affect probably over two and one-half million people. There are approximately 125,000 people who undergo a radical colostomy or ileostomy per year. I was one of them.

Even the American Cancer Society states, "Evidence in recent years suggests that most bowel cancer is caused by environmental agents.

Some scientists believe that a diet high in beef and/or low in fiber is the cause."

Doctors Tell Many People That One Bowel Movement Every Two Days Is Fine.

What Do You Think?

I think it is absolutely ridiculous. I've known some doctors to say that even once a week may be normal for you. Do they also think it is "normal" to have a bowel lined with black, hardened mucus since I'm sure most everyone undergoing surgery or autopsies has it, so it must be normal.

Years ago the famous Dr. Harvey Kellog of Battle Creek, Michigan, said, "Of the 22,000 operations I have personally performed, I have never found a single normal colon." If Dr. Kellogg made this comment around 1900 just imagine how much worse the situation is today.

Do You Believe That Colon Problems Cause Other Illnesses?

Very definitely yes. I have personally seen the following conditions either clear up completely or be greatly improved as soon as the person cleansed their bowel. Headaches, sciatic, stiff neck, arthritis, psoriasis, high blood pressure, swollen tonsils, pneumonia, flu and colds, allergies, sinus, skin eruptions, eye problems, constipation, paralyzed bowel, chronic fatigue, liver spots on head and face, leg cramps, frequent urination, chronic pain in side and more. We can't cure old age, but we can postpone it for a while. "There is really no incurable disease, only incurable people."—Dr. John Christopher

What Causes A Lazy Colon And Bowel?

The bowel soon becomes overburdened with accumulated toxic wastes and poisons. It's unable to throw off these poisons.

Let's visualize the following scenario: You have a perfect bowel, you are on a perfect diet. Once in a while you ingest something that is harmful (remember, anything that is not a food the body treats as a poison). In order to protect itself the body causes mucus to be formed in the colon long before the harmful food or substance reaches there. The substance reaches the colon 18 hours later (remember, you have a perfect colon and things move along right on schedule). The mucus has been prepared by the body and is lining the colon so you won't absorb the poison when it gets there, so it literally coats the poison. Then later it breaks down and will be discharged from the colon with no harmful effect. Well, you got away with it that time. Nature's protective mechanism functioned properly. So you do it more often.

Four times today you ingested mucus- forming foods. Most of which is also low fiber. The mucus is secreted four times today to protect you against what you just ate and drank and smoked. So you do this every day of your life.

But every day you TRY to eat something raw, one apple or orange or salad (maybe) this helps. But 85 to 90 percent of everything you eat is going to cause mucous to be formed. THE MUCUS LINING IN THE BOWEL THICKENS.

Nature's protective mechanism, which was designed for occasional use only, is being forced to work continuously day after day, year after year, with no rest and no chance to eliminate the mucus which is being laid down faster than it can be eliminated. Layer piles upon layer like the rings of a tree.

Is A Heavy Bran Diet Good For You?

You can't expect to erase the abuses of a lifetime by taking a couple of tablespoons of bran. Heavy doses of bran CAN be dangerous for a lot of people. Bran can only propel the new daily fecal matter through the already clogged colon. It will not sweep out the hardened, encrusted mucus and hard fecal impactions, nor will any other roughage. If you had started out as a child eating diets high in roughage and fiber, you wouldn't be in this shape today and large doses of bran would be fine.

I realize that some people are in such bad shape they are grateful for any small measure of relief bran can afford. They tell me, "I have to have bran every morning or I can't go at all. (How much more relief would they get if they cleaned out their entire colon of the putrid, decaying material!') If you get relief from bran, don't stop using it but be careful if the colon is looped, bent, twisted, etc. Bran can get stuck in the loose mucus (which can be in there by the quarts) and clog you up completely. The psyllium seed powder (intestinal cleanser) is 100 times better than bran. It is nonirritating and absorbs huge quantities of water, softens and lubricates.

Do Hemorrhoids Have Anything To Do With Constipation?

That would be the major contributing factor. I feel that the pressure from a backed-up distended colon and the straining from constipation (causes the blood vessels to stretch in the lower part of the colon and rectum. It then becomes enlarged, fills with blood, gets sore and itches), along with loss of muscle tone, would be the main cause

You Mention A Seven-Day Fast. Isn't There another Way To Become Healthy Without Fasting?

First of all, I would like to clarify this. True, fasting means the abstinence from any type of food or drink, except water. This program is not a true fast. Actually, I prefer to call this a seven-day cleanse. Of course during the seven-day cleanse you are drinking only liquids. Some juice, as well as water, JWT, and some vegetable broth. Absolutely no solid food.

The following is the program I recommend:

.....The seven-day bowel cleansing program done every seven to eight weeks using the Jason Winters Tea.

.....Continuation of use of intestinal cleanser once or twice a day.

.....This followed by as perfect a diet as you can manage. The complete mucus-free diet, as much raw food as possible.

.....Drink lots of pure water and exercise.

Would You Explain Your Complete Program In Its Entirety?

This cleanse can be done every two months for a year or more or however long it takes to cleanse the bowel completely. I suggest at least twice a year as a maintenance program after the initial year or year and a half. Not only does this cleanse the bowel and tissues of the body—but gives the glands and organs a rest.

EAT NO SOLID FOOD for the full seven days. Drink only filtered juices: Apple, orange, grapefruit, grape, pineapple, carrot, etc. Do not drink unfiltered (whole fruit) juices such as tomato, V-8, prune, apricot nectar, etc. JW Sprinkle is excellent. Broth from vegetable soup, made from fresh vegetables. I allow my patients to have a cup or two of hot broth made from powdered raw vegetables and barley.

The night before you start the cleanse: Take two HERBAL laxative tablets (included with the powder). The second night take one and the third night take one. If desired for stubborn cases, inject (using an infant rectal syringe) one cup of olive oil into rectum. Try to retain this until morning (massage the bowel gently).

Every day for the full seven days take:

Five times per day...three hours apart (for weights over 150 lbs.).

Four times per day...three hours apart (for weights under 50 lbs.).

1. Pour about 10 to 12 oz. of water and juice into pint jar or blender and:
2. Add one tablespoon of clay water (Bentonite, the intestinal detoxificant).
3. Add last one heaping teaspoon of the intestinal cleanser (Jason Winters colon cleanser).
4. Put cover on and shake violently 12 to 15 seconds or blend for a few seconds only (just enough to dissolve).
5. Drink quickly as it gels fast. Follow with drink of water if desired. If it gels too much before you drink it, don't eat it with a spoon. Add more liquid and thin it down.

One and a half hours after taking the above combination take:

Six Springreen tablets, or Green Life (same thing)-these are essential.

One Wheat Germ Oil Capsule.

Two Vitamin C Tablets (100 mg.).

Take this combination four times per day in between doses of the cleanse.

At the end of the first day take a coffee enema or home colonic on the home enema or colonic board. The home boards are highly recommended. They are much more effective and easier than an ordinary enema. Then each morning and evening take an enema.

The Enema

This is how to take a coffee enema:

Take one or more enemas daily for the seven-day program and the first day off and follow up for a while two to three times a week. Take more if you get a toxic reaction from the cleanse.

Use four to six tablespoons of ground coffee (not instant) to two quarts water. Simmer 15 to 20 minutes. Cool to lukewarm.

Do not have water bag hanging too high (about two feet above rectum) to prevent too much pressure.

Those of you who have already been taking coffee enemas, perhaps for years, have been instructed to do the following: Lie on side, let in coffee slowly while you draw in a deep breath. Then lie there and retain coffee for 15 minutes, then expel. The purpose of this method is to enable the caffeine to be absorbed through the hemorrhoidal veins and into the portal vein and into the liver. This stimulates the bile ducts to produce bile, causing the detoxification of the liver by causing it to dump accumulated poisons. This is an excellent method for detoxification of the liver. This will pull out a toxic reaction in minutes. Just letting in the coffee and retaining it will stimulate the bowel walls and the bowel will rid itself of some of the putrid matter. But without the massaging you cannot totally accomplish this.

After The Seventh Day Of Cleanse

Continue to take the intestinal powder and clay water morning and night until two natural bowel movements a day are established. These products are not laxatives, they are not habit forming. The powder furnishes a fiber that absorbs large quantities of water but is slippery, soft and very bulky (much more fiber than bran) and is nonirritating. DO NOT STOP TAKING EVERYTHING THE MINUTE THE SEVEN-DAY CLEANSE IS OVER. It may take years to establish normal bowel habits. Just be sure not to take this combination too close to meals so you won't interfere with food absorption.

Continue to take the Springreen or Greenlife tablets if desired. The juices from the grasses of grains are highly nutritious.

To break the fast: On the first day after the cleanse is over it is imperative you eat only small amounts of raw fruits and vegetables. Do not eat cooked food or junk food or you may get sick. I know this from experience. Take the supplements.

Second day after the cleanse: Add steamed or baked vegetables, soft boiled eggs (very soft). No bread or dairy products. Use raw veggies and fruit.

Resume normal eating, eliminating sugar, refined flour (white), artificial color, processed foods, junk food.

Drink lots of pure water (between meals).

Continue taking an enema or colonic one to 3 times a week until bowels become normal. Do not allow stools to become hard or tight. Then take colonics less often.

ACIDOPHILUS—Take a good quality Lactobacillus acidophilus after the cleanse to reestablish the intestinal flora washed out by the coffee enemas.

Put a colander in the toilet bowel to catch the mucus accumulations. Most fecal matter will wash through, leaving the accumulations. Then you can see for yourself.

Description Of Products

USE ONLY JASON WINTERS COLON CLEANSER (psyllium seed, plus husks) a powder that, when added to a large mount of water, swells up and becomes mucilaginous, soft and slippery, attaches itself to the mucus lining of the colon, softening and loosening up the hardened encrustations and fecal matter. THIS POWDER IS AN ABSOLUTE NECESSITY FOR THE SUCCESS OF THIS PROGRAM.

INTESTINAL DETOXIFICANT (Bentonite, a clay suspended in water), can absorb 90 times its weight in toxins from the intestinal tract. An infinitesimal molecule that can literally smother the germ. The active ingredient is Montmorillonite. Its effect is physical rather than chemical.

GREENLIFE OR SPRINGREEN TABLETS:
Dried extracted juice of young grains: Barley, oats, wheat and rye, raised on soil not sprayed or chemically fertilized. Rich source of vitamins, minerals and enzymes

COFFEE: Twofold purpose. 1) Stimulate bowel wall and peristalsis. 2) Stimulating bile production in liver, therefore detoxifying it.

BEET TABLETS: Taken after the seven-day cleanse to have a slight laxative effect and cleanse the liver.

If you have a special health problem, it might be advisable to consult a colon therapist.

Are Coffee Enemas Habit Forming?

At the risk of being facetious, if you drink coffee anyway, what difference does it make?

I certainly would never recommend that anyone drink coffee. So for those of you who object to coffee, don't use it, but don't let that keep you from going on the program. Use lemon juice, apple cider vinegar, bentonite, Epsom salts, or an herb of your choice. Some use chaparral or black wabut,

I've seen coffee irrigations on the board relieve toxic headache, feverishness, grogginess, leg cramps, aches and pains, etc., or even convulsions (from toxins) in just minutes.

So Would You Suggest That Anyone On The Jason Winters Program Or Any Other Health Program Do The Seven-Day Cleanse As Well?

Yes, I certainly would. If they have never cleansed their bowel thoroughly I feel they are missing the boat and that they will never be completely healthy until they do this.

I feel this seven-day cleansing program is extremely compatible with Jason Winters' program. For the simple reason that according to the way I understand it, Jason, is that your program entails a cleansing of the body with the use of the JW Tribalene, which is also a blood purifier, therefore, cleaning out a lot of toxins and poisons and rebuilding the body and giving it more strength and endurance. The bowel cleanse can speed up the detoxification process and more rapidly eliminate the toxins as they are being released. Then, after the cleanse, the Tribalene would be absorbed better along with the other nutrients. Also, I find the Tribalene gives you strength and helps sustain you while on the cleanse. You can't just cleanse all the time, you have to rebuild the body.

Dr. John Christopher states that we only absorb about one-tenth of what we eat because of all the mucus buildup, etc., in the colon. After we cleanse the bowel we only require about one-third the food we did previously (he means natural food). But is it any wonder why people are eating all the time, snacking on junk food, etc. They are not absorbing their nutrients and are constantly hungry in the body's attempt to get more nutrition. They are literally starving to death while consuming too many calories and becoming overweight.

People who have diverticulitis or diverticulosis, or stomach irritation, etc., might not want to change their diet too rapidly and suddenly launch into a high fiber diet—it might be too harsh to start with. So ease into that a little bit slowly.

If you can't eat your salads, drink your salads in the form of raw juice.

DEAD FOODS—If it won't spoil, it's probably dead.

DAIRY PRODUCTS—If possible avoid them. They are all very mucus-forming foods. They are one of the main causes of allergies, in my opinion, as well as the fact you have a dirty bowel. I've seen people go off sugar and dairy products and sometimes in a few days their allergies are completely gone.

Dr. William A. Ellis of Arlington, Texas, who has researched milk for 42 years, claims that the milk protein, casein, is very indigestible to humans, especially infants. Also, he claims it has the ability to neutralize hydrochloric acid. Milk and cheese generate a lot of mucus in the bowel and respiratory tracts. Milk can cause constipation as well as diarrhea. According to the Nevada Clinic of Preventative Medicine (a group of medical doctors who practice homeopathic medicine), in Las Vegas, almost 100 percent of all patients going through the clinic are allergic to milk. "All books on allergies I've ever studied state that milk and milk products are number one on the list of allergens. A question commonly asked me is, 'won't you get a calcium deficiency if you don't drink milk?'" Dr. Ellis States, "The calcium in cow's milk does not metabolize properly, whereas the calcium in mother's milk does. Thousands and thousands of blood tests I've conducted show that people who drink three or four glasses of milk a day invariably had the lowest levels of blood calcium. Two proteins present in cheese have been known to quite often cause headaches, Tyramine and others.

DON'T DRINK LIQUIDS WITH YOUR MEAL—They dilute the digestive juices. Drink a nice big drink of whatever you want about 30 minutes before eating. If you are eating the wrong kind of food, that is dry and has to be washed down with a lot of liquid, then that is food to avoid. Natural and raw foods don't cause you to be thirsty with your meals.

Case Histories

These are the usual type of results.

1. Man in early 40s. Badly bloated, abdomen distended, overweight (mostly from bowel and water retention). Not feeling well, joints in hands aching like arthritis. Hands badly bloated. Could barely hold a pencil to write his name. On the fourth day he could feel the fluid running out of his fingers. Got out a lot of putrid matter, etc. After seven days his bloating was completely gone, could write his name, joints didn't ache, face looked great. He lost about 15 pounds. Looked very trim.—J.M.—Kingman, AZ.

2. Early 40s. Bloated, chronic shoulder pain, distended abdomen, face bloated, puffy, constipation, high blood pressure, overweight. After cleanse: Bloating gone, lost about 15 pounds but looked like he had lost 50 because of the bloating. Feeling much better. Blood pressure better. Shoulder pain much, much improved. Face looked more glowing.—Mr. C.—Kingman, AZ, —Mr. S.D.—Texas.

3. Headaches of 20 years' duration gone. Constipation improved.—J.S.—Kingman, AZ.

4. Psoriasis on hands—After starting cleanse psoriasis started to come out of her tissues in arms. Spread over her entire arm area, bilaterally, then went away.

End Of Interview

I thought that my colon was in fantastic shape. Dr. Forsyth, however, laughed at me when I said this. She said that she could prove to me that I needed a cleanse and if I undertook this, I would be amazed at what I passed.

I decided to take her up on it. I would go for seven days without eating and I would do the cleanse exactly as she suggested.

The first two days I was hungry, but taking a half pint of juice (grape) and half a pint of water with the tablespoonful of bentonite and one teaspoonful of the colon cleanser five times each day stopped me from becoming too uncomfortable.

On the third day I went to the bathroom five times and each time the bowel movement was bigger than I usually had while not on the cleanse. I could not understand where all this "black stuff" was coming from.

When I started on the cleanse I weighed 250 lbs. The third day I weighed 246. The fourth day of the fast I started passing green mucus, about a half gallon of it. I then weighed 241. I called Dr. Forsyth and asked if this was all right. She could hear the concern in my voice and when she told me it happens to almost everyone, I felt quite relieved.

The fifth day of not eating, I went to the bathroom five times. Still green mucus, now mixed with black hard stuff. Weight at this time 237 lbs.

The sixth day I was not hungry at all. I had three bowel movements this time, all hard black fecal matter. Weight 234 lbs. I felt great and was able to get into the clothes that had been placed in the back of my closet because my waist had grown from a 40" to a 46".

On the seventh and last day of the fast I had one bowel movement and passed something four feet long. Once again a panicky call to Dr. Forsyth. She explained that this hardened mucus had been lining my colon for years and I was lucky to be rid of it.

Seventh day, 230 lbs., skin great, healthy look, dear eyes, and a determination to do this at least once each year from now on.

Take special note of the fact that if anyone ever gets up off their seats and determines to try something to make them healthier or will give them a better way of life, people gather around to try to talk you out of it.

Listen to me when I say that if they think it's all right to walk around with all that rotting fecal matter, green putrid mucus, bloated stomach, gas indigestion and bad breath, let them go ahead, but don't let them talk you out of your conviction.

I am very proud of one young lady who works at a hairdressing salon in Las Vegas. She went on the seven-day fast and cleanse and every day her workmates, without exception, tried to talk her into giving it up. Suddenly they all became experts on the subject of fasting and of how bad it is for a person. They forgot how many times in the Bible it tells people to fast.

The world is like that though. People have the urge to talk someone out of something that they can't do themselves (or think that they can't).

Notes

Chapter 12

An Evening With Tony Moscato

We were staying at the Sheraton British Colonial Hotel in Nassau Bahamas, and were very busy. Our friends from Canada, America and England had all checked into the hotel in order to help us fill the orders for the book **"Killing Cancer."**

I had never imagined the popularity and strength of a health magazine known as the **"Healthview Newsletter"** published in Charlottesville. But they had just published a great story about my beating terminal cancer and we were receiving around 5,000 orders each day.

We took over the boardroom of that hotel and hired almost every unemployed person that we could find to help us. What a wonderful time that was. Bay Street in Nassau is very popular with good restaurants and banks, but over the hill is another matter, for this is where the "ordinary" people live. Most of the huts are just made of wood with no running water or inside toilets. A complete contrast to the tourist section.

A mother came to see me saying that her daughter, Aleya Bibi, had cancer of the face and did not have long to live. She asked me to come with her, over the hill, to see her daughter. I hesitated to do this for I am no doctor, so am definitely not allowed to heal anyone. That's the law. Her tears overcame me and at last we walked over to the terrible dirty shack she called home. The young girl was in an awful condition. So bad was she that I drew away, which upset me for I was usually overcome with compassion and would hug cancer victims. But this time I drew away with dread. I wanted to run, to escape, for this little girl had the exact same cancer that I had previously had and in the same place. I quickly told the mother what I would do, if the girl were mine, and left the shed and that familiar smell of death that I had last smelled in the cobalt radiation room in America. I was ashamed, but still I fled. Soon after, I left the Bahamas and found myself on a book promotion tour of North America. This was a chance to visit my son in Las Vegas so I welcomed the opportunity. That is when I first heard of Tony Moscato.

He was handsome, slim and sounded just like Mario Lanza. He would travel California on singing engagements and would stride onto the stage with confidence and calmness. One day his face started to swell and ache. It got worse and worse until the swelling was so large it was affecting his eyes. He went through a biopsy operation and, in May of 1983, returned to his own office, turned on the telephone answering machine to hear the statement, "This is Doctor Ward. The tests show it's malignant. It's cancer. Lympho Sarcoma of the immunoblastic variety." Finding that traditional methods held out no hope for him, he decided to go the alternative therapy route.

He started reading books by the dozens and found, to his dismay, that there were dozens of alternatives, each one stating that it was the very best one, but he was fighting against time and he didn't have much money.

I quote from Tony Moscato's own newsletter:

"Which one to choose? They all seemed to say the same thing: No meat, fish or fowl. No cigarettes. No alcohol. No caffeine. No processed foods. No salt. No sugar. No dairy products. No fried foods. No canned foods. No junk food. No fast food, ONLY LIVE, HEALTHY FOODS to be ingested and enemas, implants and colonics to cleanse the bowels.

I had stopped smoking a year and a half ago after smoking for 28 years-so that was no problem. Consumption of alcohol was not a part of my life, except when forced to socially accept a drink. Caffeine was another story. I was consuming caffeine not only through coffee, but soft drinks as well. Sodas are very high in sodium.

Although I tried to maintain a balance with health foods at home, I used to indulge, while out, in junk fast food for a quick pick-me-up.

Every night I had my pint of Haagen-Daz ice cream to fall asleep. My food was not only soft to chew, but very sweet to the taste. On the weekends I loved my omelettes cooked in oodles of creamy butter and topped off with homemade jellies and jams.

With the ominous decree that I had contracted cancer, gone was the stress and depression I had been experiencing. No longer did I have to worry about the house selling or my singing act being booked or making a success with Herbalife products or even marketing my Moscato greeting cards.

All those things were no longer valid in my life. I was benched by the Great Big Manager in the sky and placed on the temporarily disabled list. Just like other players in the big leagues of sports, you can't play in the game until you can heal your injuries sufficiently to either carry the ball or at least attempt to carry the ball.

The alternative I chose was WHEAT GRASS THERAPY...because of the following reasons:

Low-cost, do-it-yourself program.
Three-week length of time.
All raw, living foods.
Enemas and implants.
Nontoxic drugless regime.
No vitamin or mineral pills to take.
No injections.
Need no helper to do the program.
Closest to nature.

After four weeks of my own self-induced Raw Foodism program, plus three weeks of the Wheat Grass Juice and Implant Therapy, my cancer cells were adjudged dead. My tumor was down but still evident.

At this point, I immediately transferred to a Macrobiotic diet for balance. My Yin and Yang forces were out of balance and my next priority was to balance my Yin and Yang. The gentleman who suggested this diet was my radionics practitioner. Curiously though, in seven weeks my tumor had almost trebled in size and I was scared to death, confused and in pain 24 hours a day. I lived like a dead man—wanting literally to die and get it all over with. I kept asking the Universe to be taken away from all this. I was losing all hope of ever healing this growth that kept growing and putting incredible pressure on my face. The pain was unbearable!

A month previous to all this sad state of affairs a psychic friend, Crystal Sterling, had told me my healing would come through Jason Winters. I had feebly made an unsuccessful attempt to contact him.

Well, after spending two and one-half hours with an orthomolecular doctor who I believed would help me and relieve me of my pain and pressure, his total negative reactions made me go within myself (my last refuge).

I met a couple, Richard and Ma Wagner, at lunch that day who had spoken personally to Jason Winters and they told me how to reach him in Las Vegas. That evening I called and left a message on their message unit to call me back collect. Jan, his wife, called me the very next morning, Thursday, and on Friday noon she was at the Los Angeles airport delivering the Jason Winters Tea and his book, "**Killing Cancer.**" (As quick as that—the Universe does move quickly when we get out of its way.)

On Monday morning Jason Winters called me and said, 'In six weeks that poison will be out of your face—you have nothing to worry about! All you have to do is drink six glasses of carrot juice daily, eat 20 raw, unblanched almonds daily, take six Tribalene capsules and have two coffee enemas each day.'

Ladies and gentlemen, within three weeks the poison on my face was gone. That was a miracle! The result of my faith in deciding to listen to my small, soft-speaking voice and, of course, following the nutritional program without deviation. The Universe had answered my prayers.

What an incredibly natural and simple program. How much time had I spent trying all those difficult, demanding and rigidly restrictive diets. In the seemingly interminable search to find my healing—the money that I had worked so hard to save was all spent: The herbalists, acupuncturists, acupressurists, chiropractors, dentists, oral surgeons, ear, nose and throat specialists, oncologists and the never-ending x-rays.

As I now look back over the whole situation, I thank God that I was given the chance of beginning again...**getting cancer was the greatest thing that ever happened to me**. And I thank Dr. Ward for being the one who diagnosed it for me because, if it were anything less, I would have proceeded on my merry ole way—not changing my life—just skirting the true issues of life and living.

CHANGE is the "open sesame"—the door key to every room in God's mansion.

CHANGE is the key word—a person's intimate involvement with the capacity to change is the answer to the question."

We Are What We Think We Are

Tony Moscato is back singing now, as handsome as he ever was, but an awful lot smarter. He tells his story on radio and TV giving hope to others. He has written a book called, appropriately, "**You Bet You Can**" and it is very interesting reading, whether you have cancer or not.

And, oh yes, by the way, if you were wondering about the

fate of the little girl, Aleya Bibi, she is now 17 years of age and very pretty. She is working as a waitress in a cafe on the Bay street.

The reader may well wonder why I put Tony and Aleya in the same chapter. Well, it was the same information that helped Aleya and Tony.

And both are determined to change the world, that the simple truth must not be hidden, that faith can heal, faith can save, and faith if necessary, can move mountains.

Their healing came from faith, a change of mind, a cleansing of the body and nutrition.

Chapter 13

Articles • Legends • Letters

Threshold To Tomorrow

by Ruth Montgomery

It is possible that Jason Winters has been an instrument in effecting more remissions from the mysterious malady called cancer than any other single individual living today. Yet he is neither a doctor nor a scientist, and his formal schooling ended at the age of fourteen.

I had not heard of him until the spring of 1981, when, after reading. Strangers Among Us, he wrote to me saying: "Four years ago I had terminal cancer of the tongue and jawbone, and a large malignant tumor under my ear. It was a hopeless case, although the doctors nevertheless insisted that they remove the jawbone, tongue, and possibly the voice box. But, first I had to have a biopsy to find the extent of the cancer. The surgeons said it would take a half hour, but I was six and a half hours on the operating table, just for the biopsy. The cancer was too extensive to operate right away, so they decided to give me seventy-five radiation treatments on my face. I was never supposed to be able to use my tongue again, because they had cut the nerve during the biopsy."

Jason said that before the cancer he was an uneducated salesman and stuntman, always broke and always traveling. "My knowledge was limited. I had a great wife and five children, and was always worried about making ends meet. After the biopsy operation I was markedly changed. I found that I had a great knowledge of herbs and the natural way to live. I combined the herbs that I found around the world, and my cancer disappeared. I became fantastically healthy. Write-ups about me in magazines brought others to me, all were helped.

"I began traveling the world, lecturing and bringing hope to millions. One and a half million people now use my herb formula, and the amazing results are all documented. Did something happen to me on that operating table? I quit school at the age of fourteen and never had further studies, yet I began to write. Suddenly I could converse intelligently with doctors, surgeons, and nutritionists. How can I explain my sudden interest in spiritual things and the abrupt changes in my attitude and personality? Everyone noticed the many differences in me. My wife was the first to notice and tell others about it, even before we read your book. Could you ask your friends (the Guides) if I am a Walk-in?"

Since publication of *Strangers Among Us* in the fall of 1979, I have received many letters from readers who implore me to ask the Guides if they are Walk-ins, but in most cases I am told they are not. When I asked about this particular letter writer, the Guides emphatically replied: "Jason Winters is indeed a Walk-in. He will go far in assisting others. That is why he came back."

Thus began my correspondence with this remarkable man, whose herbal tea and enzymes are sold in twenty-one countries to a million and a half people, nearly all by word of mouth. Even the medical profession is apparently taking notice. Jason says that his herbal formula is now being recommended by five or six hundred doctors in the United States, an equal number in England, and numerous others in Canada, and that Dr. Jan Pierce of England gives it to all his cancer patients.

According to Jason, the tea, which consists of herbs grown on three different continents, simply purifies the blood so that the pancreas can produce enough enzymes to devour the poisons in the system, and he says that there are 30,000 documented cases in America alone of those who have experienced remission of cancer by drinking several cups a day.

There is no question that Jason Winters himself, in 1976, was a dying man. A team of doctors and surgeons pronounced him a terminal case, with infiltrating squamous cell carcinoma of his tongue, jawbone, and throat. The six-and-a-half-hour exploratory operation to take a biopsy disclosed that the malignant tumor was wrapped around his carotid artery and attached to the wall of his jugular vein. The team gave him three months to live if he agreed to massive surgery, or only days if he refused.

What they did not realize was that the badly frightened patient who had entered the operating room was now replaced by another ego who had just begun to fight.

Jason Winters was born in England on September 13, 1930, to a working-class family, and was seventeen years old before he rode in an automobile or ate in a restaurant. That was the year he and his parents moved to Canada to be near his two older sisters, who had married Canadian soldiers during World War II. Then began an adventuresome life during which Jason crossed the Canadian Rockies by balloon, traversed the MacKenzie River by canoe to the Arctic Ocean, hunted polar bears in Alaska and kangaroos in Australia. He spear-fished with the Maoris, crashed Jaguar cars through brick walls to test safety belts for the New Zealand government, crossed the Sahara Desert by camel, and went to Hollywood where he played the role of Geronimo in *Apache Agent* and performed as a stunt man in Audie Murphy films.

In Hollywood he met Jeannette, a stunning model who had emigrated from England in 1946, and after marrying they continued their restless wandering, with their five children being born in three different countries. "I was always poor," Winters says in retrospect, "but I was having a ball. Everything was fun, until I developed emphysema from smoking so much, a year before the biopsy, and became depressed and run down."

While taking a steam bath at the YMCA one morning, he noticed a swelling on the side of his neck, and an ache deep inside his throat. He bought some lozenges and tried to forget it, but he couldn't help noticing that the lump was growing, and within a few weeks even his friends were calling it to his attention. Finally he went to his family doctor and was sent by him to a surgeon, who arranged for dozens of X-rays, scans, examinations at the Nuclear Medicine Center, and pills.

Then came the biopsy operation, during which a different soul reportedly replaced that of the discouraged man on the operating table. The Guides of that transition: "In a previous lifetime the new Jason Winters had been a renowned healer in Australia, and before that an herbalist. In England, where he taught and lectured on the use of natural foods and nature healings. He was also an astronomer in a lifetime in Italy, and has had distinguished careers in other fields of endeavor. He wanted to make use of his healing knowledge at this particular time, because the medical profession had be come so devoted to chemicals manufactured by man, and in some areas so commercialized, that he feared the undoing of healing advances of the past. He entered the body of Jason Winters during the long drawn-out biopsy operation, when it became apparent to those on this side [the spirit plane] that the one then occupying the body would be unable to keep it alive for more than a few weeks. The new personality entered in order to rehabilitate the body and use its mechanism to help others overcome the same sort of physical ills from which the original Jason was suffering, and he has done so. He awakened interested in ancient known herbs for healing, and brought them together into one channel that has enormous restorative powers, and with his fresh awareness he was able to infer others with his own enthusiasm and ability to live at peace with nature and the natural elements."

Before telling Jason about this message, I asked him to describe the alteration of personality that seemed to have occurred during that exploratory operation. Without hesitation, he replied: "I entered the hospital a nervous and frightened man. After six and a half hours I awoke to the news of terminal cancer with calmness, able to cope. Every morning since then I have awakened with the same dream memory. A man's voice is echoing in my wind. There is a green hill with one large tree at the top' and a man in a white robe is standing under the tree, lecturing to dozens of us who are sitting on the grass. The scene is beautiful, with colors far more lovely than here on earth."

The Guides say that because Walk-ins bring fresh awareness, they subconsciously maintain contact with the spirit plane. It would appear that Jason continues to receive instructions during the sleep state, from former associates on the spirit plane, and although his conscious mind does not recall the substance of the spirit lectures, the inner knowledge remains, to be used in the waking state.

The remarkable recovery of Jason Winters is described in a little booklet he wrote called *Killing Cancer.* In it he recounts how his doctor, after informing him that he had terminal cancer, left him to his misery and his wife, Jan, sadly went home to break to news to their five children. But when the doctor made his hospital rounds the next morning, he found Jason and another patient engaged in "a hilarious pillow fight from our wheelchairs,"

"The doctor was furious," Jason recalls. "Don't you know you have terminal cancer? Don't you realize you should be in bed?' Because I was sure that all doctors were gods, I obeyed him quickly, But it was not long before I was out of bed again—this time to trudge around the hospital. I walked around the whole place five times for exercise, and when I returned it was the head nurse's turn to be furious. She said the doctor had been complaining to her about me, and once again assured me that I had terminal cancer. It seemed to me that everyone was worried in case I forgot to die, The doctor even went so far as to lecture my wife on my behavior."

Jason says that after numerous tests the medical team decided that he should have five weeks of cobalt radiation on his neck and head. Then, if the swelling went down sufficiently, he could have radical neck surgery. "That meant the removal of my tongue, jawbone, neck muscles, and the inside of my throat," he says. "To begin with I would receive three cobalt treatments each day for five weeks. The cobalt treatment took away my taste, made it impossible for me to make saliva, burned the right side of my face and made my hair on that side fall out. I went from 263 pounds down to 170. My knees were shaky, and I could not stay awake longer than four hours at a time."

Through some inner prompting, Jason began eating spoonfuls of honey after each cobalt treatment and smearing his burned face with vitamin E. Many of his fellow patients under cobalt treatment were dying, but he was improving to such an extent that the doctors remarked on how well he was withstanding the radical treatments.

"I told them what I was doing," he said with a grin, "and they said that was fine, but not to mention it to the other patients. That remark puzzled me no end. I did tell the others about it, and they all started the same treatment, with good results. I began to realize that doctors are not gods after all. They kept telling me to get my affairs in order and prepare to die, but I decided I didn't have to die after all.

"The next day the surgeon called me into his office. He had decided to operate on me as soon as possible. Radical neck surgery. Removal of tongue, jawbone, and neck muscles. When I asked him if I would live any longer from having surgery, he said probably not. I looked him straight in the eye and said, 'No surgery.' Then I stood up and walked out of his office, My heart was singing. I was going to keep my tongue and if necessary, die in one piece.

"Many times the doctor called my wife to tell her to get me into hospital. Everyone was trying to get me there, even though everyone knew that I would die anyway. I couldn't understand it. I wondered who these people thought they were, asking me to have this terrible operation."

Determined to survive intact, Jason Winters then went the Laetrile route, and for a time with good results. The tumor rapidly diminished, but after a time came back to its original size. Jason says of this disappointment:

"It was as though I had been given life only to have it

snatched away again. This time I really did prepare to die. I purchased all kinds of religious books, and while my family went to work to keep groceries on the table, I read them all. In my misery I was struck by how many times herbs are mentioned in the Bible. Herbs as medicines show up in so many different religions that it seemed to be too much of a coincidence. Hippocrates, the father of medicine, stated that herbs shall be for medicine. So did Buddha and Krishna. Then I found that the American Indians believed in herbs and used them as medicine; also the gypsies of Europe, and the Hunzas, and the aborigines."

From his readings he decided that the most powerful ancient herb for tumors was a root that grows only in Asia, but his long-distance calls failed to locate any of the herb in the American marketplace. Then he learned that it was available in Singapore, and with one of his children supporting him under each arm he made the grueling flight. Shortly after arrival in Singapore, his wife located an old woman in a rural area who cultivated the herb recommended by the Buddha for tumors, and for two weeks he drank the mixture steeped in hot water. At the end of that period, although the tumor had not noticeably enlarged, it also had not reduced in size. They purchased some more of the herb to take with them and flew next to Tucson, Arizona, where Jason located the herb known as chaparral, from the creosote bush, which Mexican Indians drink for health, and he tried brewing that; but with no better results

Then with his money all but gone he used his credit cards to fly to England where he was introduced to red clover *(Trifohum pratense,)* the gypsy health drink, and spent the next few days brewing clover blossoms tea, then the Asian herb tea arid then the chaparral. By the fourth day he was so desperately ill that his wife insisted on their returning to American while he still had enough strength to travel. After returning home Jason went back to brewing his three kinds of herbal tea, and laboriously washing out the teapot after making each variety, but experiencing no improvement.

“I was busy making tea and drinking it all day long, and getting weaker all the time,” he recalls. “One morning I was at my lowest ebb. I thought, to heck with it, I'll mix all the herbs together and save time. I’ll never forget that it was five minutes to ten on a Wednesday morning. I made the tea combination and a miracle happened. I could feel it with that first swallow. It seemed to ring a distant bell, and awaken a long-ago memory. It screamed at me that this was what I needed. Strength seemed to pour into my body. That day I made a gallon of the tea and drank it all

When his family returned to the house they could see the difference in him, and knew that something remarkable had happened. Jason was jubilant. He knew now that he was going to live. He continued mixing the teas together, and within three weeks the unsightly tumor had vanished from his neck. In nine weeks he returned to work, feeling healthier than he had since his youth. His friends were amazed, and as word spread throughout the community, people with cancer began thronging his doorway. He had given some of the tea mixture to his parish priest, and when the padre’s hemorrhoids, from which he had suffered for twenty years, disappeared within two weeks of drinking tea, he told Jason that he must make the tea available on a wider scale, even though he could expect persecution and ridicule from the pharmaceutical and medical professions, or be guilty of the sin of omission.

After much thought I decided to tell my story,” Jason says. “A small newspaper first took up the story, which resulted in over three hundred telephone calls and a thousand letters, plus a bigger lineup outside the door from 8:00 a.m. until past midnight. My boss fired me because I was supposed to sell refrigerators, but cancer patients filled the store and we could not move. Everyone wanted the tea. Separately the herbs would not work for me. Together they were a miracle. I started importing the ingredients and mixing them in four-ounce bags, which I would give to anyone who wanted some. In exchange they would make a donation so that I could afford to buy more herbs."

A radio station next told his story, and was inundated with calls. People began flying in from Australia, Germany, and other areas of the world. The police became regular visitors to my place," he says, "making sure I did not tell anyone the herbs were any good for anything. But I didn't need to say anything. The world was so desperate for something natural that would work that I was constantly running out of herbs."

John Heinerman, a scientist writing in the December 1981 issue of *Health Express,* the journal of the International Academy of Nutritional Consultants, made a public confession of his original doubts about Jason Winters and his herbaline tea, which he now calls "miraculous." In the article he told about "Jason's terrible problems with the Canadian Protective Health Agency [the equivalent of our FDA] several years ago, when they stormed his house with a search warrant and confiscated all of his herbs and literature," and about the "hardships Jason and his family had to suffer when they fled to Nassau in the Bahamas to continue their work of helping others in the fight against cancer."

Greedy people already had tried to take him over, and had begun harassing Jason even before the raid on his Canadian home. Then friends took up a collection so that he and his family could flee to Nassau and set up a company there. Jason says of that period: "We started receiving over two thousand orders a day, and that has continued with absolutely no advertising. We had to hire all the unemployed people we could find to help us, and still the business grew. Over one thousand letters each month pour in, telling of the relief and cures obtained from all kinds of ills. Hollywood stars, politicians, all types of medical professionals, attorneys, truck drivers, etc., order regularly." Avarice prompted some people to package imitation teas under the pretense that they were the same as the Jason Winters herbal tea formula, but they apparently lack the healing magic.

Jason has an interesting theory to explain why he believes the tea works. "God placed a certain herb in each continent to cure illness by simply purifying the blood," he says. "Life is in the blood, and if anything purifies the blood then a person's God-given natural immunity will have a chance to take over and fight all disease. The herb that God put in Asia will not grow elsewhere, and the same goes for the chaparral of North America and the red clover of Europe. If you try to grow these herbs elsewhere they do not thrive because of soil deficiencies. Jesus spoke of one herb for purifying the blood, Buddha of another, and the North American spirit fathers of yet another. Now, in those days before coffee, white sugar, processed foods and fast-food outlets, any one of these herbs would have done the trick on its own. However, we who live today have such toxic bodies that we don't know what good health really is; after all, we have nothing to judge it by. We're fed on canned milk from birth, then doctored-up cow's milk and canned baby food, graduating to hamburgers, french fries, coffee, and white poisonous sugar. That is why just one of these herbs would not work on me. I was so full of toxins, as we all are, that it took the combined effort of these three most powerful herbs to bring me back to health."

Jason says that on a recent trip to England he was "met with open arms" by the medical profession, including physicians and radiologists who were eager to try his tea. One of them tested himself before and after drinking it, on his radionics machine, and found that it raised his energy level from 47 to 88. He also claimed that the tea worked on the mental and spiritual planes as well as the physical. Startled by this assertion from a highly regarded radionics expert, Jason recalled the words of the old lady in Singapore. "This herb will bring the spiritual and mental bodies into line with the physical body."

Unlike some of my remarkable new friends, Jason Winters completely accepts the idea that he is a Walk-in; as does his family. "My children are all convinced of the change," he says, "and can readily accept the Walk-in status. So does my wife. It explains so many things that had puzzled us before we came to understand that I was in fact a different person."

The Guides say of the changeover: "Jason Winters was a discouraged, frightened man when he became aware of the future awaiting him without tongue or jawbone, and was not able to face the prospects of such a disastrous operation. During that long biopsy probe, he subconsciously prayed for release from the agency awaiting him, and since it was apparent on this side [the spirit plane] that he would be able to survive no more than a few months after such a drastic operation, another volunteer entered his body and began to revitalize it. This occurs more often than those in physical bodies realize, for without this reenergizing many such patients would shortly die. The new Jason Winters was an adventuresome, optimistic soul who accepted the challenge and brought back within his awareness the knowledge of ancient herbs that have been known throughout history, but only in isolated areas. By combining those he selected through his inner knowing, he drew into the body the necessary ingredients to rejuvenate the cells and make them slough off the cancerous ones. His optimistic attitude and the reenergized cells provided the necessary stimulus, and thus the rejuvenation occurred."

Jason recalls that after news of his miraculous recovery appeared in some newspapers, he was asked to address a meeting of nutritionists. "I had never spoken in public before," he remembers, "and I was very nervous about it. I made notes of the most important points on four-by-five cards, so that I could refer to them. The night finally came and I started to talk. Suddenly I thought to myself, hey, this isn't the speech I was going to give. I kept on talking, saying things that I had no reason to know.. The audience was captivated. I still kept talking, and was as interested in what I was saying as they were. I was startled at my own knowledge, as I went into great detail about the poisons in certain foods that we regularly eat. The response to my lecture was astounding, and I received more offers for more lectures. I never told anyone except my family that this information pouring out of me was originating from somewhere else. It was at this time we realized that I was being used and was no longer my old self.

"I've recently finished two four-hour radio talk-shows in Honolulu, enough to shake the very best professional, but I was able to answer all the questions about herbs, illness of every kind, foods, reincarnation, and karma nonstop. Listening to the tapes afterward surprised me, because the answers I gave all proved correct upon checking. I take no credit for any of this, as I know it is not my doing. I know l am being used for a purpose, but l am surprised that 'they' chose a knucklehead like me."

If the former Jason Winters was a "knucklehead," his replacement obviously is not. Jason regularly addresses health-food conventions here and abroad, "and it is here that the miracle proves itself," he says. "People by the hundreds come up to me, grab my hand and start crying. At a recent Long Beach convention nine of them were crying at once. It seems they had all read my story, tried the tea, and became well. I have trouble not weeping myself when confronted with such an outpouring of love. Of course I tell them that God is responsible, and that all I did was follow what Jesus, Buddha, and the others told us to do. I am still overwhelmed by it all. Both my sisters are shocked and astounded by the change in me, as are my relatives in England. When strangers seek me out to ask questions. I am as astonished by my answers as they are."

Most of the Walk-ins whose cases I have studied were in the midst of a marital breakup at the time of the ego transferal or shortly thereafter and have since divorced. After all, it must be quite a shock to find oneself wedded to a stranger. I therefore asked Jason about his marital status, and it was his wife, Jan who replied: "Before Jay [Jason] had cancer, I was and still am a dominant person, a typical Aries, and Jay was not. Now Jay is as dominant and forceful as I am, and this does make for a lot of sparks between us. However we are beginning to understand what has happened and we are adjusting. Mind you, it takes work. It is like living with a different person, and that's what he is.

"Jay did not realize that he was now a dominant personality until we had a conversation with our son, Alan, who is studying psychology in college, and from out of the mouths of babes came this truth. You mentioned to Jay that some of the other Walk-ins have had a lot of trouble with their marriages, which has led some to divorce. Well, I can understand that, as Jay and I have had some problems, and it is difficult to live with someone who is other than the person you promised 'to love, honor, and cherish.' I am confident that we will be able to work things out, now that we know the problem. When I read your book *Strangers Among Us,* I knew you were talking about someone like Jay. And you know what' I was not surprised. I already knew that I was living with a Walk-in."

Other interesting changes occurred as a result of the substitution of souls. Jason says that although the hospital in Prince George, British Columbia, Canada, definitely diagnosed emphysema, and he found his activities severely restricted, the condition totally disappeared after the biopsy and ego transferal.

Further, although he had been christened Raymond Winters and was called Ray by family and friends, he could not seem to recognize or respond to the name after his awakening from the anesthetic. "I had an overwhelming desire to be known as Jason," he told me, "although I had never previously thought of the name. When I was called Ray it took me several seconds to respond. It was as though it was not me. Ruth, I know this sounds crazy, but the name transition was smooth and easy, with my wife and all our friends calling me Jason or Jay with no trouble at all. It is almost inexplicable, and we still do not understand it. All we know is that Ray Winters underwent the biopsy operation and Jason Winters emerged. Ray was broke, but Jason is now a very successful businessman.

"Over a million and a half people drink the herbal formula each day with results that are truly remarkable. Life is in the blood. Purify the blood and your God-given immunity will take care of any disease. The herbs purify the blood, that's all."

I asked if he really believes that the herbal tea works for everyone, and he replied thoughtfully: "No, I don't think that. Attitude has a great deal to do with it. I have a theory that if you're a jealous, bitter, or uncaring person, you are dumping poisons into your body that nothing can heal. You have to take the herbs with the same love as God gave them to us. You must have faith in yourself as well as in God and His herbs."

An unsolicited letter from Jason's sister, Edna Johnson of Surrey, British Columbia, adds an interesting footnote to the Jason Winters's story. In it she said," I spent a few weeks with him in England last year. In some ways he is the same old Ray, his given name, but he seems to know so much more than I ever remembered! We both had only eight years of schooling in England. Also, he does not remember a few things which ordinarily I should think that he would. Our mother had two items that she was particularly proud of: a very large silver tea-coffee service on prominent display and a granddaughter clock of which we were all very proud. Ray, or rather Jason, didn't even remember them; and I'd mention quite a few things that happened, which he should have recalled, but he didn't. Yet I find him so optimistic, full of life and of knowledge."

Jason's inability to recall some of the objects and incidents that seem important to members of his family is not surprising. A Walk-in inherits the memory patterns of the Walk-out, but just as we can no longer remember many happenings of our earlier years, so a Walk-in would have even greater difficulty in bringing to mind things of an unimportant nature that had not involved his or her own emotional system. After all, a Walk-in is not the person who lived through those events or shared those possessions.

In completing this chapter on Jason Winters, I asked the

Guides if they had any further comments, and they wrote: "Jason will soon develop another process with equally startling results, for his is a farseeing mind, and his dedication to helping others will make itself felt in the years to come. He will be able to assist those who will listen to develop a natural life-style, from additives and harmful chemicals, so that abundant good health will lead them toward survival in the difficult years ahead. He is able to recall ancient formulas that have healed in ages past, and to find the ingredients, long forgotten, that were put on the bountiful earth to keep humans free from disease."

I had the pleasure of meeting Jason and Jan Winters in person shortly after, and was exceedingly impressed by the handsome, tall rugged appearance of this dynamic man whose exuberant manner bespeaks sparkling health. And just as this manuscript was going to press, I received a letter from Jan saying that "the other morning. Jason awakened so excited that he jumped out of bed, exclaiming that he had been given a powerful new formula. He wrote it down, and spent the next few days at libraries reading medical journals. He found that the different ingredients in the formula have been investigated for years by separate medical researchers, yet have never been put together. Separately they proved beneficial in many ways, but Jason's plan to combine these new herbs has been greeted with enthusiasm by everyone to whom he has talked. It looks like a giant breakthrough against degenerative diseases."

Although it is too soon to assess the value of this new product, it would seem that Jason Winters is already beginning to fulfill the Guides' prophecy about him.

(Reprinted by permission of the Putnam Publishing Group from "Threshold To Tomorrow" © 1982 by Ruth Montgomery)

OLD FASHIONED
NATURAL PRODUCTS

September 6, 1991

Dear Raymond,

I had a phone call yesterday from Sir Jason from Bombay. He has found another herbal combination that has been a mystery for years.

As you know, I have been manufacturing herbal preparations for years. I look forward to these calls from Sir Jason from all over the globe. Every one of these products has proven to be of great benefit to the human race.

Sir Jason has made the creation and manufacture of herbal preparations fun. We have lived for so many years with old wives' tales and myths. Now Sir Jason has placed at our disposal new products with great potential.

Over the last 18 years, the staff of Old Fashioned Natural Products have been kept busy, testing, approving and manufacturing for Sir Jason. He has put the joy back into herbal products.

Just thought I would keep you abreast of the goings on.

Warmest regards to you and your family.

Sincerely,

John F. Logsdon

SCIENCE PROVES THAT THE INDIANS AND THE MEXICANS HAVE BEEN RIGHT FOR OVER SIX HUNDRED YEARS

Nine months alter the last Atomic blast, which turned the test area into a barren desert, scientists make a remarkable find. One small plant grows healthily where all else is dead. Intrigued by this the scientists took the plant and the seeds to their laboratory for the utmost scrutiny. What did they find?

The plant and the seeds were loaded with a substance called NDGA. This ingredient not only protected the plant from nuclear radiation, but tests showed that it is a key to longer life for humans, plants and animals.

CHAPARRAL CONTAIN N.D.G.A.

In Sir Jason Winter's book "'KILLING CANCER," published in 1983, he found that the Indians and Mexicans of the southwest used chaparral every day for good health. Even Sir Jason Winters used N.D.G.A. in his valiant flight and ultimate success from terminal cancer.

Years ago, John Heinerman, the famous author of "*Treatment of Cancer With Herbs*" stated that "Studies by microbiologist Emiliano Mora at Auburn University have demonstrated that an extract of Chaparral kills malignant cancer cells in test tubes. In experiments dating back to the 1960s, N.D.G.A. has significant growth inhibiting activity against some animal tumors, though not against others."

We are proud to present this up-to-date information which proves once again that ancient cultures, living close to nature and God had special knowledge that is only now being proven correct.

Big Breakthrough For Science

A few months ago, scientists found something they named phytochemical. It is something found in all plant life that is nothing other than an immune system. Now they tell us why eating fresh fruit and vegetables are good for you. What you are doing is taking the plant's immune system into your own body and so boosting your own immune system. Some breakthrough!. My great-grandmother knew that. So obviously, did Jesus, Buddha, Krishna and even the late comer and father of all medicine, Hippocrates. They all mentioned herbs and vegetables for health. My great- grandmother would hit us children on the head with a spoon if we didn't finish our salad. It seems that modern science in spite of itself, keeps proving the religions of the world quite accurate on health issues. They call phytochemicals a great discovery, we call it ancient history,

The Legends as told to Sir Jason Winters

by Serge Zilmann, Brussels

And it came to pass that one day a man appeared in the town of Nagpur, Central India, the year was 1066. Crowds gathered as he walked to the center of the village. They stared because they had never seen his like before. He was a giant of a man, at least six feet six inches tall, he wore nothing but a loincloth around his middle, exposing his massive muscular chest. The six donkeys that accompanied him were all heavy laden. His hair hung to his shoulders and was unbelievably golden in color. The eyes, which everyone strained to see, were bright greenish-blue. His body was also burned to a golden tan.

This was the land of dark, short people, and they were all sure that this was a god. His friendly manner encouraged them to come closer and soon the children were fondling the gold band he wore around his upper arm and his walking stick, upon which was carved the head of a lion in sold gold. The villages were astounded to learn that he was 60 years of age.

The stranger stayed in the village for 12 years, and every morning he would visit the marketplace and tell stories to the crowds that would gather and sit around him.. . .stories of wisdom, far off countries, kings and princes.

He ate little, but partook of herbal grass each day, special grass that he brought with him on the donkeys. He planted special seeds and would water the plants daily with tenderness and love. These he would also eat. Then he disappeared.

He left behind him 18 children that he had sired, many of them light-skinned and blue-eyed. It is still possible to meet his descendants to this day in Central India. They called the herbs he planted "Golden Lion" after the stranger. Men who took these herbs fathered many children, well into old age.

Fourteen years later, after his disappearance, he arrived in the town of Pingu, China, hundreds of miles away from nagpur, India. When he disappeared one night, after 12 years, he left behind him 17 children.

Nine Hundred years later:

Jason Winters was in Brussels, Belgium, when he was told of the legend.

He asked for the name of the two towns and declared on the spot that he was "going to check this out." He continued, "Don't you realize the importance of this, if it's true? Don't you realize how it could help millions of men around the world?" I can remember the look on his face as he realized the he was the only one interested in this legend, and that his companions had returned their attention to their brandy served in warmed-up giant snifters.

It was five months later when I next heard from Sir Jason. He faxed me a report of what took place when he arrived at the two towns, one in India and one in China. He also sent me a report done by a laboratory. Every herb used by this Golden Lion was good for the male sex drive. It looked very promising indeed. Chills went down my spine as I read it all. How on earth did this man, 900 years ago, know all of this? Modern science is only now finding out about it.

The last page of the fax was of a lion, dressed in a private detective's raincoat, collar up, belted, and complete with trilby hat pulled rakishly down over one eye. Actually it was the look on the lion's face that made me laugh. It showed that the lion was "pretty hot stuff." Under the picture were the words, "Sir Jason Winters is proud to present to all the men in the world . . . The return of the Golden Lion." (Why the return of the Golden Lion? Obviously, with blond hair and blue eyes, the legendary man was originally from Scandinavia. He had taken the formula to Asia 900 years before—Sir Jason was just now returning it.)

Nine months later we received the news that Sir Jason and his wife had a baby boy, named Jason Junior. One year after this we received another report that they had another son, whom they called Walter Winters. My wife thinks that this is funny because Sir Jason is 60 years old. I am secretly taking the Golden Lion formula myself.

The following are just a few of the eighty-thousand letters Sir Jason has received

Dear Jason:

Just a note to say thanks again - Boy, that convention was very hectic. Have been meeting very interesting people. So my cancer and its healing lead me to things that are new - different and exciting. Getting your book to a lot of people and they are all very impressed with its content and its inspirational words.

Tony and Barbara
California

* * * * *

Dear Mr. Winters:

I have been taking Tribalene Tea for the past month and a half and great results have been obtained. I am alive. The results obtained from drinking the tea have enabled other means of physical treatments to be more easily tolerated...

Ontario, Canada

* * * * *

Dear Jason:

God Bless you! I think your Tribalene and Xian are fantastic, for 26 years doctors have had me on tranquilizers. I Just couldn't seen to function without them, until our friend Tom came to Puerto Rico for a holiday and he introduced me to your Tribalene. When he returned to Milan, Italy, he sent me your literature and the rest is history. Please send me two Tribalene and two Xian.

Judith
Puerto Rico

* * * * *

Dear Mr. Winters:

I have just read your book, *Killing Cancer,* and I want you to know I think it is one of the greatest health books in the natural line ever written, perhaps the greatest. I enjoyed it so much. I intend to buy up a number of these books and pass them out to friends who need them and also to the various health stores I trade with. I also intend to write a review of the book for health magazines. I just finished one by a Dr. Kellogg, late president of the Battlecreek Sanitarium entitled, *The Natural Diet of Man.*

Phoenix, Arizona

* * * * *

Dear Mr. Winters:

Six months have passed since we began to sell Herbal Tea and the quantity of sales has increased every month satisfactorily. The drinkers' delighted voices of recovering their health encouraged me and our will of selling.

Holding the next two creeds, I have appealed to make efforts to my employees and persons concerned, that is: the sooner and the more people; serving my efforts to recover people's health by herbal tea—present of nature.

I heard you're visiting Japan on October 20th. We will welcome you, Mr. and Mrs. Winters, willingly.

Hirosuke
Japan

* * * * *

Dear Mr. Winters:

Earlier this year while recuperating from major surgery for bowel cancer, I heard about your "Victory over Cancer" report, and through this I learned about herbalene tea.

Unfortunately, I did not know about your herbalene tea before my operation, however it certainly helped to speed my recovery. My relatives and friends have remarked on how well I look, my color is good, my appetite is excellent, and my weight is back to normal. I take five glasses of your tea daily.

To maintain this feeling of well being, and for my future good health, I intend to always take your herbalene tea as part of my daily regimen.

Sincere thanks for making these wonderful herbs available to everyone.

Michael
Ontario, Canada

* * * * *

Dear Jason:

I have been drinking your herbalene tea for the past four months, and have experienced benefits from doing so.

Your tea has helped to disperse a condition of varicose veins in both my legs, which I have had for twenty-five years.

I have also had a good increase in my energy level. I recommended the herbalene tea in the promotion of health through natural sources.

Chris
Canada

* * * * *

Dear Jason Winters:

Please rush me a bag of your blood cleansing tea. The one with red clover and chaparral combined.

I feel so much better while I'm taking it. Not tired like I used to be. It feels so good to feel good. I'm a mother of 8 children and can't afford to be tired...

* * * * *

Dear Mr. Winters:

I have just finished reading your book, *Killing Cancer* for the umpteenth time, and am very impressed with this material which is passionate, straightforward and simply honest.

I recently saw a health magazine ad for a bound volume of all of Mr. Winters' books which have been published to date.

Paul
Pennsylvania

* * * * *

Dear Mr. Winters

My wife, Irma, a cancer patient, has received and tried some of your tea with excellent results within a week. There has been an extensive reduction of glandular size especially in the lymphatic system...

George
California

* * * * *

Dear Mr. Winters.

I have been on your tea for seven days and feel 100% better already. It has really stopped the pain. The doctor stated it was arthritis and I had to live with it. It looks like I may not have to live with it after all. My skin cancers are turning red and look like they are healing well. The doctor's salve is helping too, but when I drink your tea I feel no pain.

MAN, IT'S GREAT.

James
Louisiana

* * * * *

Dear Mr. Winters.

No doubt you receive hundreds of letters similar to this one but I must add my word of praise for your wonderful tea.

I have been afflicted with a nervous stomach disorder for a number of years, the attacks becoming more frequent, more severe and lasting longer as time goes on. Until recently I have become completely incapacitated and unable to eat, sleep or walk across a room without becoming breathless. Doctors and medication were of no value whatsoever.

I started on your tea two weeks ago and already I am on the road back, as I am able to type this letter and do light household chores

I hope eventually to be able to take full care of the house as well as a part-time job.

Thank you and God Bless!
Louisiana

* * * * *

Dear Mr. Winters:

The doctors are costing us a bundle and about all we get are guesses and promises. For three weeks, I had been slipping my wife a few cups of your tea and within that three weeks she began to really get better and to express a desire to live.

Wayne
Boynton Beach, FL

* * * * *

Dear Jason:

I have been drinking your herbalene tea since last September, with FANTASTIC results!

For much of this year, I had a terrible problem with my eyes that three specialists could not help me with. My eyes were always red, swollen and watering, and painfully sensitive to light. I couldn't wear my contact lenses, watch television or be in sunlight without discomfort. I had to wear sunglasses even on cloudy days, and I sometimes had to call in sick at work.

After drinking your tea, my eyes completely cleared and I haven't had a problem or better eyesight since! To me it was a miracle.

I have had other benefits from the tea as well. It has somehow helped me to maintain a weight loss of 15 pounds, which I had been trying to get rid of for four years.

I have had a great increase in vitality and can function on less sleep. My skin has never been clearer, and the eczema I've had for sixteen years has diminished to almost nothing.

Margaret
Ontario, Canada

* * * * *

Dear Mr. Winters:

Since I'm not sure where to begin, I will start with a deeply felt THANK YOU to both you and your son. I thank you for your making Jason Winter's Tea available in the U.S. I am profoundly grateful to Ray for introducing me to your products. If he were not the warm, compassionate person that he is, it is quite unlikely that I ever would have learned about your natural healing products. That I met Ray when I did is in itself a miracle. To appreciate how true that is requires a bit of my medical history...

I was diagnosed as having Hodgkin's disease at the age of 37. Previously, my health had been essentially perfect. I was treated with radiation therapy at Stanford University Medical Center. Later, the treatments cleared up the tumors that had been so terribly obvious in my chest x-rays. Because Hodgkin's is a curable disease, I thought I was done with it, so I returned to "business as usual."

I was not to be so lucky: In the spring, I developed a non-Hodgkin's lymphoma tumor in the lachrymal duct of my right eye. Over the next few months, tumors appeared in several other areas of my body, including two of my vertebrae. At that point, I began a 7-month session of chemotherapy. While I tolerated the regimen rather well (not missing a day of work and experiencing unpleasant symptoms for only 8-12 hours after the drugs were administered), the drugs significantly reduced the working portion of my bone marrow. Nonetheless, in early 1985, I was once again symptom free.

But I was to learn that an "indolent" lymphoma does not disappear that easily... found an enlarged lymph node in my groin which again lead to chemotherapy, this time using a different set of drugs. Again my response was very good—manageable symptoms (although I did gain 25-30 pounds in 6 months) and the apparent elimination of tumors. At this point, it finally dawned on me that I was going to have to do things differently if I intended to last much longer.

In late July of 1994, I again discovered an abnormal lymph node in my groin! That was indeed a day of depression... The return of lymphoma was confirmed in early August. This time, treatment options were more difficult:

Because my bone marrow was functioning at approximately 40% of its original capacity, a bone marrow transplant was discussed. As you may know, that is not a procedure you would want for anyone you care about. We could have tried the latest in chemotherapy, but why should I expect it to be any more successful than the previous two rounds? In addition, it would further reduce the function of my remaining bone marrow. Finally, additional chemotherapy could lead to the transformation of my indolent lymphoma into an aggressive form, a common result.

It was at this point that I had the extreme good fortune to share my dilemma with Ray.

Please understand that I don't go around discussing this problem with everyone. It is nothing short of miraculous to me that I met Ray at exactly the time I needed to. To do so, I had to move to Las Vegas when we could have moved anywhere in the country; we then had to move to the right part of Las Vegas; next we needed to join the Green Valley Athletic Club; then I needed to work out on the same days arid at roughly the same times as Ray did. Finally, we needed to meet one another as well as discuss this very personal problem. The amazing thing is that all these things happened at the best possible time for me!

As a result, this time while the doctors were waiting to see how the lymphoma would develop, I began drinking JW Tea daily, taking Beta Carotene tablets and vitamins C and E purchased from the health food store that Ray recommended, preparing and drinking a glass of carrot juice regularly, spending up to an hour each day listening to meditation and attitude adjustment tapes, further decreasing my working hours and increasing my time invested in exercising. I have made a concerted effort to reorient my thinking from business success to personal survival. Fortunately for me, the result has been well worth the effort.

In February of this year, I was absolutely ecstatic to have the radiologist report that my CT scan was NORMAL! Now it is up to me to do everything I can to maintain this result. I will do so through continued education on my part of the healing potential of various natural products, particularly those from Sir Jason Winters! I feel confident that I can remain symptom free with this new approach made possible by my acquaintance with Ray and subsequent use of Jason Winters Tea, etc.

In conclusion, please accept my profound thanks for allowing me to find and utilize this new, natural approach to managing my disease. It has quite literally given me a new lease on life.

Robert C. CLU, MSFS

* * * * *

Dear Jason:

Thank you so much for sending me your tea. I GOT RID OF MY CANCER! The doctors were so amazed they warned me it might come back, so now I want to order more of your tea bags.

I recommend the tea to everybody I know that has cancer...so by now I do not have any left. Please send me the story of your travels so I can get somebody to copy it for me, to give away eternal thanks to you for curing my cancer!

Pam L.

* * * * *

Dear Mr. Winters:

Thank-you and God Bless You for what you are doing for others. I first read your story in Swanson's Health Products Newspaper and promptly bought your tea, strictly as a good health measure.

For the first time in 23 years I'm able to straighten out my knees completely!

Alys D.

* * * * *

Jason Winter:

I cannot speak highly enough of what I feel this Herbal Tea has done for me. My health is so much improved. My body was a mass of blistered sores, almost unbearable to touch.

I make a huge jug of Jason Winter tea, daily, and drink it whenever I feel like a drink. I've use the herb leaves to bathe and gently wipe over the sores, let it dry on, the relief is fantastic. My throat was noticeably healthier after 3 months continued use, and the sores cleared up externally after 1 month.

Anonymous

* * * * *

Mr. Jason Winter:

My wife has been drinking the tea for three months and now the cancer in the chest has gone. You are a good man to do this and we are very happy for ourselves. I will tell all my friends about the tea as is good for everything and I like it so much. Thank you and hope to see you when you come to Hamburg. I will show you many people who are interested in a healthy way of life and greet you happily.

Ralph S.
Germany

* * * * *

Dear Jason Winters:

Again, thank-you so much for the life-giving herbal tea. Vern had his checkup Dec. 12th and they pronounced him all clear. We are so grateful. It was the most wonderful Christmas gift we have ever had. May you and yours have a most joyous holiday.

Vern and Virginia R.

* * * * *

Dear Mr. Winters:

Three years ago, a relative was dying of Leukemia. She was introduced to the herbal tea by a friend. In a short time not a trace of leukemia could be found. Today, she is healthy and able to do anything a 69-year-old person does...

I am sure that God is blessing your efforts -

Oklahoma

* * * * *

Dear Mr. Winters:

My husband had a malignant tumor between the lungs. He had 20 cobalt treatments in October and November of 1983 and was diagnosed as cancer of the lungs.

The first of March he started taking your Herbal formula, Digestive enzymes with red clover and the Herbal tea. On the 29th of March, 1984 X-rays detected no tumor and he is to return for more X-rays in July. We were also told on the 29th of March by the doctor, that the tumor had been expected to grow and a possibility of chemotherapy. We feel very fortunate and thankful that the tumor is gone due to the J.W. Therapy.

C.W.
Florida

* * * * *

Dear Jason:

Thank God you were put on earth at this time. If ever the people need help it is now.

One week ago I started taking your Xian capsules. I can see a brightness in my face, I have more energy and I feel great. I can see the difference in myself.

Martha
Texas

* * * * *

Dear Mr. Winters:

Firstly, may I say how much I have been enlightened by your book *Killing Cancer.* Your astonishing story and the great faith you had in the herbs and God to cure you is an inspiration to us all. Being a true believer in God myself, I was overjoyed to know that you regard God as a vital part of your life and recovery. Your herbal tea has made me feel so much better in so many different ways every time I drink it.

Brad
Australia

* * * * *

An excerpt from Asia's top selling book: INTEGRATED HEALTHCARE IN THE PHILIPPINES

by Josef de Ubaldo

The medical education received by most physicians today emphasizes knowledge, technical skill, and experience—particularly in the field of surgery. Siegel, who was a surgeon, comments that such an emphasis "doesn't humanize care, it mechanizes it." He further suggests that medical students should first study how it feels to be a patient to be able to fully appreciate the feelings of a sick person—rather than being mere observers of human suffering. Siegel feels that a physician's training is incomplete without a spiritual discipline in the curriculum, considering that religion plays such a strong part in most people's lives.

On the other hand, religion should not impose rules on the spirituality of believers at the expense of their general well-being. Spirituality SHOuld be differentiated from religion because the former relieves patients from negative thoughts and fosters positive thinking that is necessary for general well-being.

Siegel's book *Peace, Love and Healing* suggests that changing one's state of mind can change what takes place in one's body. Through the experience of mind-altering processes, such as meditation, hypnosis, visualization, and psychotherapy. Individuals open themselves to the possibility of health and healing. The book is replete with scientific anecdotes and research concerning the relationship between mind and body. Siegel's main thesis is clearly manifested in this book—through the mental and spiritual experiences that are peace and love, healing is possible.

The Case of Sir Jason Winters

The British holistic health advocate, adventurer, author and entrepreneur Jason Winters achieved his fame and success after a nearly fatal operation for Cancer in 1977. He experienced what can only be considered as an out-of-body experience and believed that his spirit was replaced by the spirit of a humanitarian Indian physician. "Winters resolutely sought out a cure for his cancer and eventually found that mixing sage, herbalene, and red clover purified his blood and boosted his immune system.

Winters story was widely covered by the press and studied by British and European scientists A company began manufacturing mixtures of the herbal tea combination that saved him, Tribalene, which was later found to have powerful antioxidant properties. Winters continued to lecture to physicians and healers, travelling and communicating regularly with Prince Charles who was also greatly interested in the integration of alternative and allopathic medicine.

Winters has become a powerful advocate of holistic healing. His perception of the phenomenon that cured him of his illness is not restricted to herbal medicine—he advocates a brand of "common sense" spirituality that is necessary for a long, fulfilling and happy life. His appearance today at the age of sixty is proof of the success of Winters' beliefs. He does not arrogantly attribute them, however, to himself; instead, he unequivocally states,, that

Everything that Jesus, Buddha, Krishna, Bahai U'llah" told us about herbs, medicine and health is now being proven every day by doctors, nutritionists, the (U.S.) Surgeon General, His Royal Highness—Prince Charles, one hundred and fifty thousand Chinese herbalists, the Maoris of New Zealand, the Aborigines of Australia, the Hunzas and the world's' top scientist's. It's about time we listened.

* * * * *

Published and distributed by REX Book Store, Inc (RBSI)
with the main office at 856 Nicanor Reyes, Sr St., Sampaloc Manila
Tels. 741-49-16, 741-49-20.
Regional Offices: Sanciangko St., Cebu City, Tels 760-63
771-29; 156-A C.M. Recto St., Davao City, Tel 221-02-72
2nd St., Ledesco Village, Jaro, Iloilo City

Also distribute by Herbal Beau (Phils) International, Suite E, *G/F,* Dona Felisa Syjuco Bldg., Remedios cor. Taft Ave., Manila, PHILS, Tel. 50-12-61 (loc. 109, 110, 111), Fax No. 526-7069.

From a new book published in the Philippines

A Walk-in From England

More encounters with the unknown, by Jaime T. Licauco,

I just talked to a Walk-in," I told my wife.

"A what?" she asked me with her eyebrows curled.

A Walk-in," I repeated, "and in the flesh. I even interviewed him on my radio program."

I was talking about the world-famous Englishman, Sir Jason Winters, a confirmed walk-in, who miraculously healed himself of terminal cancer in 1977 by using herbal medicine obtained from three different continents.

Okay but what is a walk-in? The term was popularized by American writer Ruth Montgomery in her book *Strangers Among Us: Enlightened Beings from a World to Come,* published in 1979.

According to Montgomery "A walk-in is a high-minded entity who is permitted to take over the body of another human being who wishes to depart. They are enlightened beings who, after successfully completing numerous incarnations, have attained sufficient awareness of the meaning of life that they can forego the time-consuming process of birth and childhood, returning directly to adult bodies."

That's heady stuff likely to be dismissed as nonsense by the average person, but Montgomery's spirit guides have told her that several known world figures were in fact walk-ins. And they gave the following examples:

Mahatma Gandhi, who led a passive resistance that freed India from British colonial rule; Benjamin Franklin, American statesman, author, publisher, scientist and inventor; Abraham Lincoln, who abolished slavery and led the US into a bloody civil war; and Emmanuel "Swedenborg, the scientist/mystic who talked with angels. Others he mentioned in her book were Meister Eckhart, Shankara, and the Biblical prophet, Joseph.

According to Montgomery a walk-in returns to physical being "in order to help others help themselves, planting seed-concepts that will grow and flourish for the benefit of mankind."

Montgomery's guides said not all walk-ins are famous people

or world leaders. “Many are working quietly among us today going about their unsung task of helping us to understand ourselves, to seek inner guidance, and to develop a philosophy that will sustain us through the trying times ahead.”

She said that walk-ins seldom reveal themselves because, “to do so would imperil the good work for which they returned to physical being.” Or they may not even be aware that they are one, even several years after the substitution.

“In fact,” she said, you may even be a walk-in yourself. ”An unknown correspondent who wrote Ruth Montgomery a letter and who turned out to be a Walk-in herself explained the process of the switch-over.

“A walk-in,” according to her, “is a highly evolved entity who, always with permission, enters the body of a human who wishes to check out before completing the tasks he has begun. Sometimes the human has lost heart, or has taken on a task more difficult than he was prepared to handle. Sometimes it was the purpose of the departing human being to begin the task and prepare the body for the entity The walk-in first completes the tasks of the body's previous owner, and then goes on to do what he must do with his own projects.”

“Perhaps,” concluded the writer, “it's time to tell the story of these remarkable beings while they are among us."

The technical term for this soul substitution is “metem-psychosis,”' which is defined as “transmigration of souls.” The well-known Tibetan esoteric writer, Lobsang Rampa, is a walk-in, according to his own story. The Tibetan Lama occupied the body of a badly depressed English doctor named Cyril Hoskins who, after the soul substitution, changed his name to Tuesday Lobsang Rampa and wrote some 15 books on Tibetan esoteric teachings, astral projection, and paranormal powers.

Sir Jason Winters is world-famous for his discovery of an herbal tea bearing his name which has been proven effective in treating a number of debilitating illnesses, including cancer, and which is now marketed worldwide. But very few know the real story behind the transformation of an obscure high school dropout and terminally ill Hollywood stuntman into an articulate, healthy and highly knowledgeable herbal expert and businessman.

During a trip that he made to the Philippines to promote his well-known herbal tea products and visit his family (he married a Filipina), I was able to meet Sir Jason Winters and interview him on my regular Sunday evening radio program. He began telling me his remarkable story which he has repeated over a thousand times in many parts of the world.

"In 1977," began Sir Jason, "I had terminal cancer of the tongue and jawbone, and a large malignant tumor under my ear. It was a hopeless case, although the doctors, nevertheless, insisted that they remove the jawbone, tongue, and possibly the voice box. But first I had to have a biopsy to find out the extent of the cancer. The surgeons said it would take half an hour, but I was six-and-a half hours on the operating table, just for the biopsy The cancer was too extensive to operate on right away so they decided to give 75 radiation treatments on my face. I was never supposed to be able to use my tongue again because they had cut the nerve during the biopsy

"The cobalt treatment took away my taste, made it impossible for me to make saliva, burned the right side of my face and made my hair on that side fall out. I went from 263 pounds down to 170. My knees were shaky, and I could not stay awake longer than four hours at a time."

Through some inner prompting, Sir Jason began eating spoonfuls of honey after each cobalt treatment and smearing his face with Vitamin E. The other patients were dying, but he was not as badly damaged, prompting the doctors to remark that he was responding to the medical treatment very well.

When the doctor told him later that he had decided to operate on him by removing his tongue, jawbone and neck muscles, Jason asked him, "Will I live any longer after the surgery?" The doctor replied, "Maybe not." So Jason Winters said, No surgery." Then he walked out of the doctor's office with a smile.

He searched for alternative cancer remedies and even tried Laetrile, which he said had helped him, but not enough. He began reading the Bible and discovered that the Holy Book mentioned herbs for treatment 27 times.

In his search for an alternative cure for his cancer, he travelled to several countries in Asia, where he had heard strong herbal cures were existing until he finally combined three of the most powerful herbs he found and, in no time at all, completely recovered from cancer.

Sir Jason said, In my readings I was struck by how many times herbs are mentioned in the Bible. Herbs as medicines show up in so many different religions that it seemed to be too much of a coincidence. Hippocrates, the father of medicine, stated that herbs shall he used for medicine. So did Buddha and Krishna. Then I found out that American Indians believed in herbs and used them as medicine, also the gypsies of Europe, and the Hunzas, and the aborigines."

After the biopsy, he was a completely changed man. "My attitude towards life, my values and even my taste in food changed," he told me during the interview. "I used to like fish and chips and all those types of food. Afterwards I began to like Indian food. Up to now I still eat Indian curry every day. There are periods of my childhood I couldn't remember, but I remember a childhood in India."

He wrote Ruth Montgomery, who had written a book about walk-ins in *Strangers Among Us,* and wondered if he was one. Ruth Montgomery consulted her spirit guides and they said, 'Yes, Jason Winters is indeed a walk-in." So she included a chapter about him in her next book, entitled *Threshold to Tomorrow,* published in 1982. I had read both books long before I met Sir Jason Winters.

Jason was born Raymond Winters in England on September 13. 1930, to a working class family, and was 17 before he rode an automobile or ate in a restaurant. His family moved to Canada to be near his two sisters, who had married Canadian soldiers. Then began his adventures, which included crossing the Canadian Rockies by balloon, traversing the Mackenzie River by canoe up the Arctic Ocean, hunting polar bears in Alaska and kangaroos in Australia. He also went spear fishing with the Maoris in New Zealand, crashed Jaguar cars through brick walls to test safety belts, crossed the Sahara Desert by camel, played Geronimo in a Hollywood film, "Apache Agent," and performed stunts in Audie Murphy films. "I was so stupid at that time," he remarked to me during the interview.

The change from that "stupid" Raymond to the enlightened Jason Winters took place, according to the guides of Ruth Montgomery; during that long biopsy operation he underwent. "Raymond," they explained, "was a discouraged, frightened man when he became aware of the future awaiting him without a tongue or jawbone. He could not face such a prospect. During that long biopsy probe, he subconsciously prayed for release from the agony awaiting him, and since it was apparent on this side (the spirit plane) that he would be able to survive no more than a few months after such a drastic operation, another volunteer entered his body and began to revitalize it."

When he was told by the doctors after the biopsy that he had terminal cancer, he took it calmly and without fear, which was unlike him.

The new Jason Winters that emerged out of that operating room was "an adventurous, optimistic soul who accepted the challenge and brought back within his awareness the knowledge of ancient herbs that have been known throughout history as medicinal."

"By combining those herbs he selected through his inner knowing," continued the guides, "he drew into the body the necessary ingredients to rejuvenate the cells and make them slough off the cancerous ones. His optimistic attitude and the reenergized cells provided the necessary stimulus, and thus the rejuvenation occurred."

He changed his name to Jason for reasons he was to learn only later on. The soul that took over his body, he found out, was a highly educated Indian doctor and herbalist, named Jason, who treated white men when there was great racial hatred between the Indians and the British. Jason was killed in 1935 at the Gateway to Bombay. As Jason Winters, he visited that same place twice without knowing why.

Sir Jason Winters is one of the few who accept and talk about their walk-In status without batting an eyelash. "It's the only explanation that makes sense to me about my transformation," he said.

* * * * *

Published and exclusively distributed by
ANVIL PUBLISHING, INC.
3/F Rudgen II Bldg.
17 Shaw Blvd., 1600 pasig City
Philippines
Telephones: 631-7048. 633-6121, 633-6136
Fax: 631-3766
E-Mail: anvil@fc.emc.com.ph

Chapter 14
Fear

From what I understand, many readers of my books are atheists, agnostics and so on. It is my job to get a message across to these people without them seeing the word, GOD, and quickly turning the page. To those I ask you to please read this short passage which I think will possibly change your life.

It was by no accident that God said that we must have faith, for it means far more than the average person thinks it does. You see, faith is the opposite of doubt, so if you do not have faith then you have doubt.

You can no longer rely on anything, because doubt prevails subconsciously in everything you do. Now constant doubt causes worry—worry causes stress, and stress causes illness and death.

Where there is faith there is no fear, where doubt prevails there is always fear. This is a proven, undisputable fact, proven by the great thinkers of the world, and also proven in my own life.

Fear is the cause of all our problems. It is what causes a good looking teenager to smoke pot, or to stick a needle full of cocaine into his veins. Peer pressure and the fear of not belonging, of not being accepted.

We fear because we doubt and we doubt because we do not have faith enough.

Fear causes stress and we now know that stress destroys the body and mind, resulting in most serious illnesses of today. I have found that people who have an unnatural fear of cancer, get cancer. You see, without faith we are nothing. Without faith in ourselves, our fellow man, our God, we become full of despair, suffer from great depression and can't see any reason to carry on.

If you would rid yourself of fear, stress and illness then

you must have faith. If you say that you cannot have faith then it is simply that you have not understood what you have heard and read in the past. Start your own research into religion. Suddenly you will realize that all of this could not have possibly happened by accident. It would take all the geniuses of the world to make one human hair, then they would fail. Don't listen to atheists who say there is no God, for I can tell you first hand that there are no atheists in the front line, nor are there any in the terminal cancer ward.

After a lifetime of fighting God, it took me about 15 seconds to become a Christian, right after the doctor looked at me and said, "YOU have terminal cancer, I am going to remove your tongue, jaw bone, tonsils and the inside of your throat and you will still die in three months."

Suddenly, I started talking to God, without hesitation, and now I am well, with no operation, no disfigurement, just abundant health.

And so, the lack of faith is tied directly to fear, then stress, then illness. Have faith and you won't fear your peers, you won't need to be an alcoholic, you won't need to be psychotic or neurotic, you won't have to be uptight all the time, trying to prove yourself every day. At last you can relax and start doing a better job of living.

What else can I say about fear except that it is at the bottom of all man's problems today. The natural fear that stops you from standing in the middle of the highway is good fear, it protects you, but the constant fear of life, disease, losing your job, your spouse, your manhood, is unhealthy and will eventually lead you to the grave.

Over the last 10 years, more and more men are complaining of losing their manhood, because they associate with the so-called "liberated woman," who is so dominant and demanding that men are frightened that they won't measure up to this type of woman. Then and there a doubt is formed in the man's mind and he can't perform. These men are rushing to doctors' and psychiatrists' offices by the thousands because they feel that they are not real men any more. Thereby, the liberated woman is ruining things for herself. She has fought against being treated decently and now people are frightened to open a door for her or to call her miss instead of Ms. or to treat her like a lady.

Today they ask the man to dance, they ask the man to bed, and they scare him to death and don't let these macho men fool you. Having to perform every night for dominant women eventually causes a breakdown of confidence, the emotions, and brings on great fear. Fear eventually causes illness. And so, as explained in another chapter, the very thing these liberated women are after is being deprived them. Cause and effect. The sad, distressed faces to be seen at any singles bar shows that this is not the way. They are all sitting there through fear. Fear of being alone, of not being loved, of not having sex. Faith eliminates all of these doubts and all of these unhealthy activities.

Faith will bring confidence, wisdom, happiness and vibrant health.

Notes

Chapter 15

Treatments

Charles Hears of Cancer Diet

CANCER patients told Prince Charles how a vegetarian diet and meditation helped them "control" their illness.

They told him of their experiences when he opened the controversial Cancer Help Center in Bristol.

Earlier the Prince had been criticized for performing the ceremony by a leading cancer specialist. Professor Timothy McElwain, of the Royal Marsden, Sutton, Surrey, said he would be giving the seal of approval to unorthodox methods which might raise false hopes in patients. But the Prince went ahead with his visit to Bristol, watching meditation classes, visiting the kitchens, and seeing counselling and therapy sessions.

Prince Charles told 53-year-old patient Eric Burbridge of the Fairbank Hotel, Crantock, Newquay, Cornwall, that he looked "extremely well."

Strict Vegetable Diet

Mr. Burbridge said he had had cancer growths on his back and shoulders and was told there was not hope after several operations.

But he began a strict vegetable diet at the clinic and his growths "exploded" and were rapidly disappearing.

"1 feel terrific. I would not be here today but for the treatment I've received," he said.

Among the supporters at yesterday's opening was Dragoon Michael Bentine, a personal friend of the Prince, who said his daughter Elaine, 41, died from cancer six weeks ago in a Surrey hospital.

His other daughter Fusty, 33, was now in America where

her cancer was being controlled in a clinic similar to the Bristol center.

He said that both women had received personal letters from Prince Charles "mostly about positive thinking."

In his speech, Prince Charles said doctors and healers should work together toward their mutual goal to heal the sick. Alternative methods of treating cancer should not be dismissed as hocus pocus.

ALSO, can you imagine the courage it took for a world-renowned figure such as Prince Charles to step forward and in front of the world take a stand for alternative therapies? Have you any idea what attack he came under just prior to attending the opening of the clinic by all the medical authorities who tried to stop him? He went through with it, however, and now the doctors are all agreeing that he did the right thing. (If you can't beat them, join them!!!)

Non-Toxic Metabolic Treatment And Diet (The New Zealand Guide)

This is also a successful way of overcoming cancers, vitamins, minerals and enzymes.

Vitamins to take: Vitamin A, Vitamins BI, B 2, B17 (laetrile), Vitamin C, Vitamin E, except for cancer of the breast and/or uterus (because of its hormonelike effect).

These are extremely effective in halting and shrinking cancer—especially Vitamins A, E, and B-17; Vitamin C enhances their efficiency. They should be prescribed by your practitioner in massive doses initially, and then reduced as your cancer shrinks away. N.B. Vitamin B17 (laetrile) is most effective when intravenously injected.

Minerals to take: To assist the body by promoting the manufacture of enzymes used by the immune system in the destruction of cancer cells. Magnesium, Potassium, Phosphorous, zinc, Selenium, Calcium, Chromium (amounts to be prescribed by your practitioner following blood analysis).

Enzymes to take: These help to break down the walls of the cancer cells by digesting their mucoprotein content. Bromelain, Trypsin, Chymotrypsin, Retenzyme or Wobe Mugos (the latter is more effective but over twice as expensive), Pancrex V (dosage to be prescribed by your practitioner).

Typical daily amounts of vitamins and enzymes would be as follows for an adult cancer patient. Remember, however, to consult your practitioner as every patient has individual needs.

Brewer's Yeast tablets 3x3 daily are a cheap source of the Vitamin B group and include Chromium, protein and an anti-diabetic factor. If these are taken, no Vitamin B-1 needs be added.

Vitamin A 25,000 IU (1,000 mg).

This is best taken in the form of liquidized carrot juice with a little cold-pressed vegetable oil whisked into it. Taken this way the maximum effect of the vitamin is made use of by the body to attack the cancer. The Vitamin A tablets tend to be stored in the liver for gradual release and are therefore not so effective.

Vitamin B-1—10 to 20 mg.

Vitamin B-2—30 mg.

N.B. Vitamins B-6, B-12, and Folic Acid increase the growth of cancers so do not take these.

Vitamin C—2 to 5 grams per day (2,000 to 5,000 mg.).

Magnesium Orotate—1,000 mg. per day.

Zinc—15 mg~ (but only in cases of zinc deficiency).

Calcium—I 500 mg.

Selenium—200 micrograms.

Manganes—5 to 20 mg.

Jason Winters Red Clover Enzymes (two tablets three times a day **between** meals, i.e., on an **empty** stomach. Start with a much lower dose and gradually increase to this amount).

D—Amygdalin injections or tablets.

Although Amygdalin can be intravenously injected, the Cancer Help Center, Bristol, is currently suggesting the following: 15 apricot kernels orally administered three times a day or 250 mg. Amygdalin tablets thrice daily over an extended period, plus two grams of Vitamin C, plus 20 to 30 oz. of emulsified carotene (as described earlier) per day, plus enzymes. If large doses of Amygdalin are given intravenously, the products of cyanide detoxification (thiocyanates) gradually accumulate and there is a loss of appetite. The combination of Vitamins C, A and enzymes is necessary for Amygdalin to work satisfactorily.

Carcinogens To Avoid

1. Carcinogens in daily use or commonly occurring:

Tobacco smoke, whether or not you are the smoker. (Especially bad for lung and bladder cancer.)

Coal tar and petrochemical derivatives used in toothpaste, hair oils, lipsticks and cosmetics, perfumes, soaps, deodorants, antiperspirants and mouth sprays.

Plastics such as cellophane, nylon, Teflon, Dacron, polyethylene, polystyrene, polyvynilchloride, e.g. food containers, kitchen utensils, clothes, carpets, furniture, curtains, bedding, etc.

Fluoride in water supplies.

Fluoride in toothpaste.

Epoxy resins, glues, etc.

Dust of all kinds (including wood dust, leather dust and especially asbestos dust).

Talcum powder or products containing talc.

Carbon tetrachloride (used in cleaning fluids, etc.).

Many factory emissions.

Car, lorry, bus and boat exhausts.

Aerosol sprays.

Food dyes.

Detergents for washing food utensils (they form free radicals from food in the body).

Food preservatives, especially nitrates in bacon, tinned meat, ham, sausage, etc., but also other chemical additives.

Fumes from central heating boilers (oil, coal or gas-fired).

2. Industrial carcinogens.

Tar, tar gas, pitch, asphalt, creosote, copper, Aniline dye, Nickel, Radon (used in building materials), plastics, Radium, Uranium, x-rays, mineral oils (including motor oils and greases), arsenic, asbestos.

3. Medical carcinogens:

Reserpine (suspect), chloroform, liquid paraffin, all mineral oil products, hormone therapy (including contraceptive pills), Selenium Sulphide (suspect), methapyrilene (suspect), x-rays (including radioactive dyes and radio isotopes), all coal derivatives, antibiotics and sulphonomide drugs are strongly suspect (certainly they cause animal cancers), Depo Provera is strongly suspect. It is banned in the U.S.A. (injectable contraceptive), Psoralens (used for treating skin complaints), Aldactone and flagose cause cancer in animals. These are widely used drugs.

4. Other carcinogens:

Background radiation from A and H bomb explosions, polluting atmosphere, crops, meat and water; certain fungi as in some pickled vegetables, especially aflatoxins; Bracken (contains cocetin), certain viruses, radiation from TV sets, clocks and watches, etc.; radiation from the sun.

5. Carcinogens and potential carcinogens in food and drink:

Dyes (e.g. butter yellow), preservatives, e.g. nitrates in bacon, sausages, ham and tinned meat and other preservatives, chlorine in tap water, pesticides and their residues, insecticides, smoked meats and fish (such food often contains creosote and formaldehyde), nitrates are formed from nitrates and combined with amines in gut to form nitrosamines. Nitrosamines are cancer-inducing, saccharin (chemical sweetener), fats heated to high temperatures (above 200 degrees C or 392 degrees F) in preparing food. Frying is therefore NOT RECOMMENDED. Coffee is suspect because, in the roasting, matrol is produced. Decaffeinated coffee also contains matrol; fluoridated water, saturated fat (found in dairy produce, meat and meat products, pastry, cakes and puddings, cheese, milk, eggs, fish and chips and other fried foods).

Chapter 16

Facts That You Should Know About Cancer Research

Many doctors say that the next big illness to come along within the next 10 years will make cancer look insignificant. They say it will take that long for the microwave ovens to really start showing just how dangerous they are.

We have discussed the most necessary thing in the world and that is, of course, live food. Today 25 percent is dead and worthless.

With any food, it's the enzymes that still live that are so important to our even staying alive. Cooked food on a conventional stove leaves some enzymes alive, but a microwave oven kills all the goodness at once, within the first 30 seconds. Everything that you eat from a microwave oven is not only useless, but your body has to work very hard to get rid of it quickly, otherwise you become toxic and that is the beginning of death. These are facts that are widely known by people in authority—but they will not speak out, for they are frightened to take an unpopular stand on any Issue.

The following are also facts that have been published and are quite well known in influential circles but nothing is done for the same reason.

Is it possible that anyone could still believe that nuclear testing and nuclear power plants are as wonderful as some try to tell us?

Cancer And 'The Conqueror': An 'Epidemic' From Nuclear Radiation?

NEW YORK (AP) cancer hit an unusually high number of the cast and crew of the movie "The Conqueror," which starred the late John Wayne and which was filmed in 1954 near St. George, Utah, a year after nuclear weapons tests upwind in Nevada, People magazine reports.

Of the 220 cast and crew members, the magazine said it was able to contact 150 and that 91 of them had contracted cancer.

Forty-six of those who contracted cancer—including John Wayne, co-star Susan Hayward and producer-director Richard Powell—died of the disease, the magazine said yesterday.

"With these numbers, this case could qualify as an epidemic," the magazine quoted Dr. Robert C. Pendleton, director of radiological health at the University of Utah as saying.

"The connection between fallout radiation and cancer in individual cases has been practically impossible to prove conclusively. But in a group this size you'd expect only 30-some cancers to develop. With 91 I think the tie-in to their exposure on the set of 'The Conqueror' would hold up even in a court of law."

A report similar to People's was published in June 1979, in London newspapers, but was met with skepticism. A spokesman for the Wayne family said then that he had heard the theory but considered it "absolutely not true."

More than 950 residents and former residents of Utah, Nevada and Arizona have filed $2 billion in claims against the federal government, seeking compensation for damages they say are related to fallout. The first of those cases is scheduled to go to trial next September.

Actress Jeanne Gerson, 76, who also appeared in "The Conqueror," told the magazine that she had hired a lawyer to file a class-action suit against the government and said she hoped others involved in the movie would join her. She said she has undergone surgery for skin and breast cancer.

A House subcommittee said in August that the now-defunct Atomic Energy Commission "not only disregarded but actually suppressed" all evidence of harmful effects of radiation from atmospheric tests in Nevada.

The magazine also said the disease has struck the children of some of the actors who had accompanied their parents to the filming site in Snow Canyon near St. George, 137 miles downwind from the Yucca Flat weapons test range.

Wayne's son Michael developed skin cancer in 1975, it said. His brother Patrick underwent surgery 11 years ago for a breast tumor, but it was not malignant. Tim Barker, 35, son of Hayward, had a benign tumor removed from his mouth in 1968 but told the magazine, "I still smoke a pack a day."

Wayne died in June 1979 after suffering cancers of the lung, throat and stomach.

War On Cancer Called "Worthless Sham"—Press Telegram

Critics label prevention way to end disease.

WASHINGTON (AP)—Medical experts told a House subcommittee Tuesday that the nation's war on cancer is being mismanaged and is nearly worthless.

One of the harshest critics of the National Cancer Institute (NCI) and the National Institute of Health (NIH) was Dr. Irwin D.J. Bross, director of biostatistics at the Roswell Park Memorial Institute for Cancer Research in Buffalo, New York.

Bross said much of the money Congress has earmarked for cancer research has been "wasted on scientific boondoggles, such as the worthless cancer vaccine program" and other activities he said are pushed by technicians seeking part of the anti-cancer money.

If half of the time, effort and money for the NCI in the past five years had been put into an effective primary prevention program, "we would at this moment be well on our way to the actual conquest of cancer," he contended.

"The programs for environmental carcinogens are

little more than public relations gimmicks—paper tigers designed to reassure the concerned public that something is being done when it isn't," he said.

"This is standard policy in NIH. The program on cigarette health hazards is a farce. It consists of noisy scare campaigns which are counterproductive—like most cancer education," he said.,

Bross alleged that federal cancer research money is going to "laboratory scientists who have no real interest in...hurnan cancer and who couldn't care less about prevention of human disease."

He charged that NCI funds are largely controlled by the American Cancer Society and said it should be barred from getting NCI grants for the next four years. In any other part of government, Bross said, it would be a corrupt practice for persons giving out the money and persons getting it to be the same.

The critical analysis was given a House Government Operations subcommittee as the director of the National Center for Health Statistics conceded that figures indeed show that there is an increased risk of dying of cancer.

The intergovernmental relations and human resources subcommittee, chaired by Rep. L.H. Fountain, D-N.C., is conducting three days of hearings on the $800 million program NCI is managing.

The director of the statistics center, Mrs. Dorothy P. Rice, said the cancer death rate has risen since 1930 from 100 deaths per 100,000 population to 171 deaths per 100,000 for 1975. Preliminary figures indicate that last year's cancer death rate also rose substantially, she said.

Asked the reasons for the upswing, Mrs. Rice said that most of the increase has been due to the aging of the population. The chances of dying from cancer are highest in older persons. Other causes include cigarette smoking and more exposure to industrial environments, she said.

Dr. Sidney M. Wolfe of Ralph Nader's Public Citizen's Health Research Group called the national cancer war a "sham battle."

"NCI, under new leadership, must choose to become the leader in the war to prevent cancer, rather than the banking operation for the largely unsuccessful war to treat it (cancer) after it happens," said Wolfe.

He said the NCI should assume a "new role" in actively overseeing "lethargic" regulatory agencies by publishing an "Annual Report of Potential Cancer Victims.

Wolfe suggested that the NCI issue a public warning to pinpoint the known cancer-causing agents to which millions of Americans are exposed because of "negligence" of agencies charged with regulating hazardous chemicals.

He cited eight agents—including arsenic, benzene, chloroform and estrogens—which he said "are exposing more than 17 million Americans to a serious risk of cancer." Adding two commonly used red dyes "probably increases this total to over 100 million people," he said.

Wolfe and Bross both accused the government of yielding to pressures of profit by emphasizing after-the-fact diagnosis and treatment at the expense of preventive measures during the first five years of the proclaimed "Conquest of Cancer" effort.

Bross has persistently opposed X-ray screening of younger women in the breast cancer program—a procedure that has recently been discontinued for routine use on women under 50.

Bross charged that the screening program and attempts to develop a cancer vaccine were "boondoggle" examples of the "incredibly bad management that has plagued the Conquest of Cancer' program."

He urged more "public accountability" by government agencies that "continue to see themselves as the patrons of the medical establishment and not as servants of the public."

This theme has been sounded frequently as more cancer-causing agents have been identified and the death toll has continued to grow.

Fountain said that "in 1957, the same proportion of cancer cases—one in three—was being cured," he had been informed. If that information is correct, he said, "we will want to know why, despite all of the effort and money devoted to cancer research in the past 20 years, the cure rate has remained unchanged."

The Entrapment Of Americans

When Mildred's daughter had been sent home to die, because the doctors could "do no more for her," Mildred had become desperate. She had heard terrible things about the clinics in Mexico, how they were run by frauds and charlatans, but she decided to take her daughter there, rather than just give up.

She not only saw her daughter get well on laetrile, but also met many thousands of Americans benefiting as well. Mildred, in her simplicity, not understanding the medical, drug-oriented system of today, decided to go into the business of helping others who were suffering also. She started selling laetrile to dying cancer patients in America. Many recovered. It was wonderful. Mildred had at least learned that you are not allowed to make claims for any natural product unless you are a doctor.

An old lady came to her and pleaded, "My young son is dying of cancer, will this stuff you are selling help him?" Mildred's reply was that she was not allowed to answer that. The old lady burst into tears saying, "Please tell me if it will help my son." Mildred remained firm in not making any claims. The lady begged and pleaded with Mildred for two hours until Mildred, out of the goodness of her heart, almost in tears herself said, "yes, I think it will help him." At which point the lady stopped crying and said, "I have what you said on tape. You told me that laetrile would cure cancer. You will now be arrested." The lady was with a government department and this little bit of human feeling cost Mildred her lifetime savings for lawyers to defend her against "prescribing medicine without a license." She is now a destitute and ruined woman. This is entrapment.

Another clinic was helping people after they had been sent home to die. Remember that all these people were pronounced terminal by their doctors and so it is not the best position to be in for a clinic, as they come to you on death's door, hoping for help. Many live but, of course, some die as they were supposed to. The government agency that is set up to destroy all "alternative therapies" uses this fact to their advantage. On the few that die, the agency calls the survivor's family and asks if they would like to sue the clinic for murder!. And so, like Jesus, who was crucified for trying to bring unorthodox help to people, so are these people today crucified. One lady was set up like this in 1984 in Utah. A kinder, sweeter lady you could not find, yet because she stopped by the way to offer help to a dying cancer patient, who it was just too late for, they issued a warrant for her arrest and destroyed her name on television by saying to the world, Mrs.________was caught taking money from dying cancer patients. The poor lady was distraught, never dreaming in a million years that her country could do this to her. This kind, 50-year-old woman had to go into hiding for months, staying away from her family, friends and home.

I tell you this truth because I know that the word "entrapment" has been in the news a lot lately and I know that you will believe it. Do not think that it is easy for anyone who dares to be different because it is not. Gino Bruno was burned at the stake for daring to say that the world was round. It takes guts and courage to try to help people today, let alone to try it when they are already dying. If you do help you can be attacked by multimillion dollar organizations that will frame you, destroy you and call you a murderer. Would you dare to do it? Most alternative therapy people feel that in order to save one life it is worth them risking everything. It is something that can never be stamped out because the truth will never stay hidden.

Give respect to most people in the alternative health field. They dare to do what the Bible says, they dare to be different. Each day for them could be the day that they weaken and admit, "yes, this may possibly help you" and that statement may result in jail and persecution. If they were frauds it would be better for them to sell imitation gold watches, than to make less money doing this and to take such terrible chances bucking a billion-dollar evil enemy.

Persecution Of The Innocent

This is how the drug companies with the help of the news media crucify the good men who are trying to do what God and Hippocrates told us to do—use herbs.

"PERSECUTION" OF 5 IN CANCER FRAUD CASE CHARGED

—by Robert W. Stewart-Times Staff Writer

A *"freedom of choice"* group that champions the controversial compound laetrile as a cancer treatment came to the defense on Monday of a Colton doctor and four others charged by the Los Angeles County district attorney's office with marketing a fraudulent cancer therapy.

"We know that there is a hit list that functions between state and federal authorities and this 'hit list' includes the names of medical practitioners involved in so-called unlicensed, alternative cancer therapies," said Michael L. Culbert of the Committee for Freedom of Choice in Medicine, Inc., formerly called the Committee for Freedom of Choice in Cancer Therapy.

Among those physicians, Culbert said, is Dr. Bruce W. Halstead of Colton, near San Bernardino, who is among five men charged last month with more than 50 counts of conspiracy, grand theft and other crimes in connection with the marketing of ADS.

Culbert said his group will take action, including filing a complaint with the United Nations to halt the "*persecution*" of doctors who favor unconventional treatments for cancer.

Authorities charged that Halstead and the others violated state laws that make it a crime to market as a cancer treatment any substance that has not been specifically approved for that purpose by the California Department of Health Services. Dist. Atty. Robert H. Philibosian has labeled ADS worthless in the treatment of cancer.

Among those who appeared Monday at a press conference called by the Culbert's group were Garry David Middleton, 35, of Australia and Robert A. Sanford, 46, of Chatsworth, two of Halstead's codefendant. Halstead was not present.

It was the first time since his arrest that Middleton, described by prosecutors as the central figure in the ADS operation, had appeared in public to answer questions about the treatment.

Among other things, Middleton said, "ADS is a liquid 'that cannot be analyzed by normal methods.' " He said he does not know specifically what herbs are in the ADS tea that he sold, but that Halstead has a complete list supplied by researchers in Japan. In an earlier interview, Halstead said that his only source of information about the specific herbs in ADS was Middleton.

He offered ADS even though it did not have governmental approval as a cancer treatment because he thought it more important to try to save lives than to comply with government regulations.

Investigators for the district attorney and the State Health Department made the mistake when they said in affidavits filed in court that ADS was imported through U.S. Customs as a catalyst used to dye paper.

Instead of making money on ADS, which he sold for as much as $300 for a one-litre bottle, Middleton said, "I think I've lost most of my life savings trying to save lives." He said he gave away many bottles of the treatment.

The Committee for Freedom of Choice in Cancer Therapy, which came to Middleton's defense Monday, in the 1970s sought to legalize the use of laetrile, a substance derived from apricot pits, in cancer therapy.

The first study of the compound recognized by mainstream cancer Scientists concluded in January 1982, that laetrile is useless in the treatment of cancer.

—Please note that laetrile was tested in 29 *other countries and was found to be a valuable cancer fighter. All those countries are socialized medicine countries which means they are interested in anything that will prevent illness or heal it inexpensively.*

Beware Of Some Alternative Therapies

Those of you who have read my first book, **"Killing Cancer,"** know of the complete despair that I went through upon learning that doctors were not perfect and often made mistakes. I was even more upset to find an even worse condition prevailing in the alternative health field.

You must not, under any circumstances, believe that all alternative therapies are beneficial. Do not be taken in by all the new products that are constantly mentioned in cheap national newspapers. Most of the products benefit only the manufacturer and salesman.

My newsletter goes out regularly to well over one million homes and, because of this, I have received some pretty astounding offers from people in the alternative health field. Two well known clinics offered me $1,500 for each terminal patient that I would send them. When I asked where on earth they would get that kind of money from, they casually shrugged and said that they would simply add it onto the terminal person's bill. I need not tell you that I had nothing to do with them again. They forget that I am not one of them. I became interested in this field because of my terminal illness. They became involved for other reasons. Any clinic that is charging $3,000 a week cannot justify such charges and should be viewed with suspicion.

Before you get involved with a clinic, ask them their percentage of recovery. Get some names and addresses of people who have been made well and go to see them. If they look like death warmed over, the chances are that they have not been helped, but are just hanging on long enough to pay the clinic's charges. You would also think that people in the alternative health field would stick together. After all, they have the giant A.M.A., the government F.D.A. and the drug companies to fight every inch of the way. But nothing could be further from the truth. There is more jealousy, animosity and hatred between individuals, clinics and vitamin companies than you would believe

I am often contacted by a health magazine and asked to place an ad with them. They tell me that if I take a full page ad, costing $2,000 or more, then they will give me a great write-up in the special article section telling the readers just how wonderful my discoveries are. I always ask them if they have tried my products to which they reply that they haven't. In other words, they are prepared to say something is wonderful, just for the sake of selling an ad.

When you read one of these magazines look first for the ads, then see if the writer has done a story on the product somewhere else in the book. If you find that they have then back away, for you know now that they have "arranged it all."

One thing that will surprise the reader is that if you look carefully you will find the same writers, editors and "experts" listed in the front section of most magazines. Their names keep cropping up. This means that in America the alternative health field is run by a very few people who are determined to stay at the top. They view any newcomer with fear and jealousy. Some absolutely brilliant people in America are never given a chance because of this small mindedness. Many of the writers and editors own the companies that the magazine raves about. I have mentioned a few of the best clinics in the back of the book but please, check these out carefully too, for situations do change and so does the staff.

The best criteria is that if you should visit a health convention this year, you will be quite surprised to find how sickly the people running the booths are. They are standing there 12 hours each day to sell you something for your health. If they look sicker than you, then stay away from them. One famous health person I spoke to at the Pasadena Convention had breath so bad it could have easily killed a buffalo, showing a plugged colon among other problems. Why should you go to his clinic if it doesn't work for him?

One very strange man, short and skinny with a dirty looking beard, runs around the convention halls shouting out football scores in order to steal customers from other booths and once he has attracted their attention he leads them back to his booth like lambs to the slaughter. Sometimes, to look ridiculous, he stands on his head. The T.V. cameras love him for it is their chance to make the whole alternative health field look stupid.

A religious sect actually stole all of our advertising leaflets because we would not let them handle the Jason Winters line exclusively. They only returned them when we threatened to call the police.

If that shocks you, then please read what an English magazine published after doing considerable research.

Englishman tests automobile safety belts in Auckland, New Zealand.

Sir Jason Winters drove a new Jaguar car through a 12-inch thick brick wall at 40 miles per hour. Over one-thousand people watched as firemen had to cut him out of the car with welding torches. They cheered as he stepped out, unharmed. Debris from the impact of the crash flew over three hundred feet. Results: Seat belts work!

The Jaguar after Jason Winters stunt.

In Belgium receiving Laureate

"The Kiss" from the Grand Master —Malta

Left to right: actor Charleton Heston, Sir Jason Winters, Congressman John Ensign

Jason Winters discovered Mexican Indian herbs while working on a Hollywood film with Audie Murphy. Here, he posed with one of the Indian "extras" who brewed potent tea from herbs every day on the set.

Jason's Herbal Clinic in Malaysia

The author's wife seen here explaining the value of different herbs in Cebu, Philippines.

Radio Bombay—The old man was in terrible pain and was obviously dying. He lived under a sheet against the wall. He told me about reincarnation then he died.

Reincarnation?

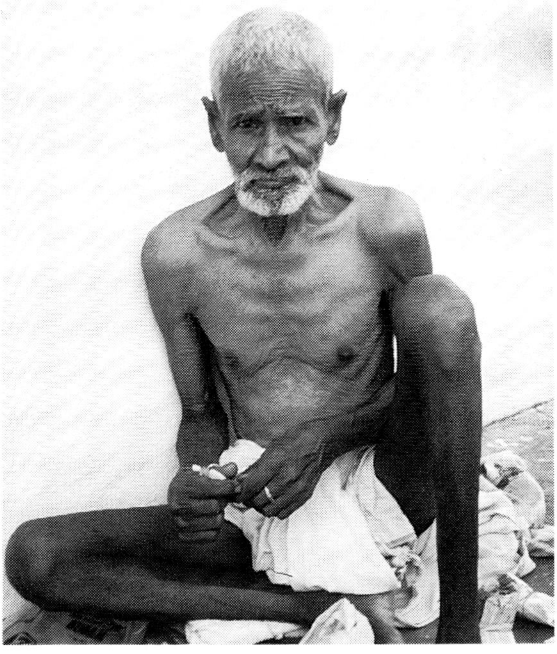

The old man squatted in the dust beside me, and as we gazed down the street of cages in Bombay, he began to speak. "You know my son, this life is an illusion - it simply prepares us for the real life in spirit - The eternal, everlasting everconscious life beyond the grave. Without loss of awareness we are there, free, happy and painless, happy in the complete knowledge that life is everlasting." His sparkling eyes shone from amidst a thousand wrinkles, and he whispered "This great truth is hidden from man for fear he may try to reach the spirit world too soon. He must do his schooling on earth first." Tears came to my eyes as I realized that I had always known this truth, deep inside, we all do.

Certificate of Special

Congressional Recognition

Presented to

Sir F.R. Jason Winters

for meritorious achievement

DATE MEMBER OF CONGRESS

Congressman James H. Bilbray (D-Nevada, together with Congressman Richard A. Gephardt (D-Missouri), are honoring Sir Jason Winters by a Special Congressional Recognition Certificate for meritorious service in creating employment in the U.S. by gaining one million Asian customers.

Sir Jason receiving Knighthood—Malta

I saw a field in which nothing would grow, because sacred cattle had been slaughtered there. Only a few wild berries that man could not eat for they would not leave the body, and their juice would stain your very soul.

Sir Jason and his staff in the market in Kuala Lampur, Malaysia. Tea Tree Oil is very popular there.

In Bombay, India, we showed the Jason Winters' Herbal Tea to street vendors. This lady smelled the tea, realized that it was good for her and started eating it.

Hospital staff and doctors attend Sir Jason's lectures—Fiji

Looking for herbs in China

1000 Chinese families live here: rent is $15.00 per month.
No crime— no drugs—no gangs— no teenage pregnancies.

This lady in Malaysia supports her whole family by selling garlic in the street. People on the way to work purchase a clove of garlic as we would purchase candy. Garlic is one of the most powerful health foods. You can see her family's wash drying on the mail box as she waits for customers.

This lady carries heavy loads like this for 14 hours every day, six days a week. Total income: Eight dollars per week. It's time for all of us to stop feeling sorry for ourselves.

People living on a garbage dump in Manila. The flies drove us crazy.

We were surprised to find that at the communal laundry in Bombay, India, many would add Tea Tree Oil to their wash to kill germs that abound in the intense heat.

Hong Kong invites us to lecture on herbs.

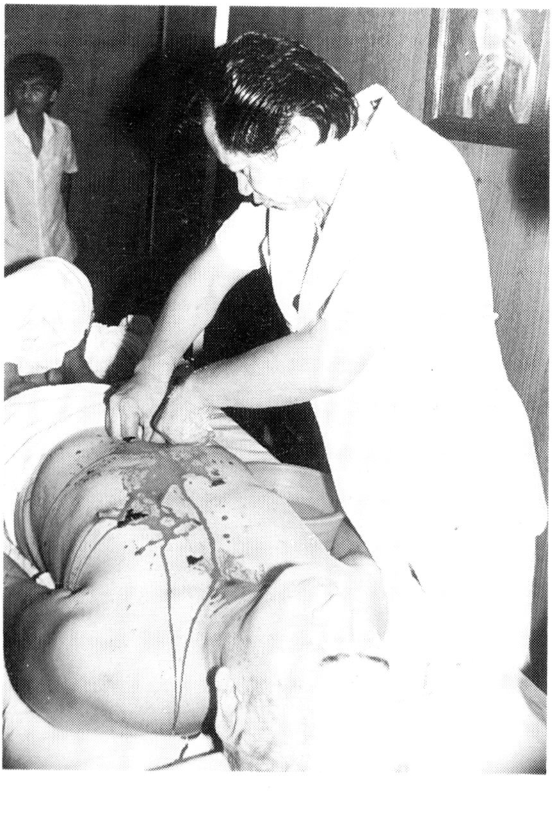

Knifeless surgery in the Philippines. Accompanied by Channel 7's television crew, we witnessed over 50 operations and were amazed and astonished.

98-year-old Chinese lady picks through the garbage.

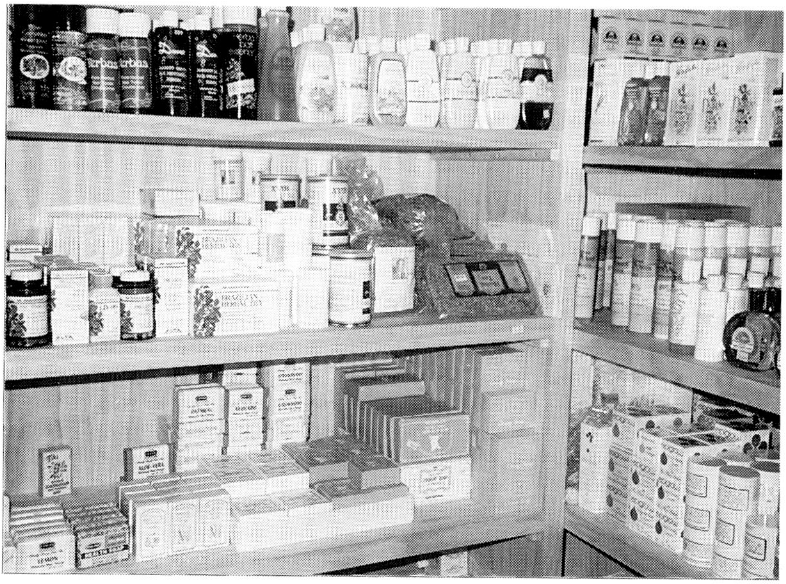

Jason Winters products displayed on store shelf in Mongolia

Jason's distributor next to the statue of Ghandi.

180 million people in Indonesia heard our talk on herbs. Here Sir Jason is relaxing.

Sir Jason Winters and Count Alberto Carlos at the Italian Embassy Ball in Manila.

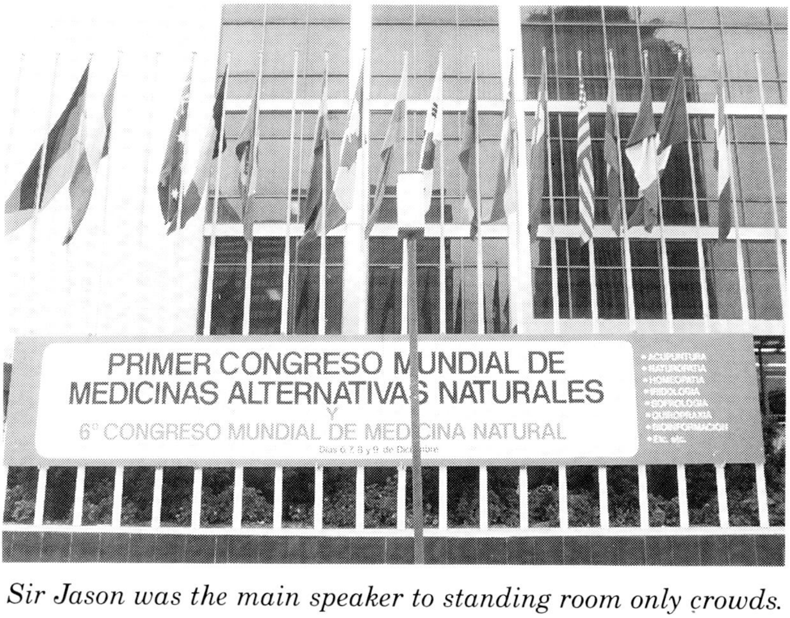

Sir Jason was the main speaker to standing room only crowds.

Raymond Winters gives a lecture to government officials and the press in Bangkok, Thailand.

Touring the White House

World's Oldest Woman — She's 131

Francisca Mota is an astonishing 131 years old, the world's oldest woman — yet amazingly, she's never been to a doctor in her life.

"Whenever I'm sick I drink herbal teas and pray to God — He's the only Doctor," says Francisca, a white-haired Brazilian farm worker.

SECRET OF LONG LIFE is the desire to live, says Francisca, 131.

World's Oldest Woman

The cottage where Englishmen come for Tea.

Sir Jason para-sailing in Malaysia, 20 years after he should have died.

Chinese man bathing in highly polluted canal. Dead pigs and raw sewage go into it every day—Burma.

Bernard Jensen, Prince Obaze and Sir Jason.

Jason and son Robin just prior to having an audience with the Prince of Borneo.

The Golden Lion Children—Jason's sons born while author was in his sixties.

CHAPTER 17

YOUR WEAKNESS AND YOUR HERB ACCORDING TO YOUR BIRTH SIGN

THE HERB JUST MEANT FOR YOU

Thousands of years ago, the Chinese Emperor Sheng Noong compiled a list of 365 herbs and their known uses. He came upon this knowledge from his ancient ancestors who, through trial and error over the centuries, found the true value of each herb.

One almost forgotten piece of information passed down to him and to almost every ancient tribe from each continent, is that people born under certain signs have certain body weaknesses and only certain herbs can help them.

To know the herb that is meant for you can be important. Also, knowing the weakness in you due to your birth sign is proving not only invaluable but remarkably accurate.

Here then is the ancient list of herbs according to the 12 signs of the zodiac.

ARIES

The complaints of Aries are: Fevers, problems of the face and head. ARIES HERBS ARE: Cayenne, Honeysuckle, Garlic and Blessed Thistle, with Garlic and Honeysuckle being the most important.

TAURUS

The complaints of Taurus are: Problems with the neck and throat due to overeating or other excesses, Sometimes an emotional problem. TAURUS HEALING HERBS ARE:

Thyme, Tansy Plantain and Silverweed with Thyme being the most important.

GEMINI

The complaints of Gemini are: Bronchial infections, nervousness, pains in the arms and shoulders and incorrect breathing causing brain fevers. GEMINI HEALING HERBS ARE: Meadowsweet, Skullcap and Flax with the Skullcap being the most important.

CANCER

The complaints of Cancer are: Indigestion, weakness of the chest such as asthma, cancer and stomach troubles. CANCER HEALING HERBS ARE: Violet, Butterbur and Ground Ivy with the Violet being the most important.

LEO

The complaints of Leo are: Sore eyes, fevers, cramps, palpitations and heart problems. LEO HEALING HERBS ARE: St. John's Wort, Mistletoe and Eyebright, with St. John's Wort being the most important.

VIRGO

The complaints of Virgo are: All problems of the liver, intestines and solar plexus. VIRGO HEALING HERBS ARE: Fennel, Marshmallow and Blue Flag, with Fennel being the most important.

LIBRA

The complaints of Libra are: Kidneys, stones, pains in the back, bladder and over acidity. LIBRA HEALING HERBS ARE: Burdock, Pennyroyal, Archangel, with Burdock being the most important.

SCORPIO

The complaints of Scorpio are: Problems with the generative organs, piles, catarrh in the bladder, uterine. SCORPIO

HEALING HERBS ARE: Wormwood, Toad Flax, Red Clover, with Wormwood being the most important.

SAGITTARIUS

The complaints of Sagittarius are: Goiter, pain in lower limbs, fevers and overexercise, also cancer of the intestines and liver. SAGITTARIUS HEALING HERBS ARE: Agrimony, Red Clover, Chaparral, and Tribalene, with Tribalene being the most important.

CAPRICORN

The complaints of Capricorn are: Corns, warts, skin diseases, ruptures and weakness of the lower limbs. CAPRICORN HEALING HERBS ARE: Slippery Elm, Shave Grass, Thyme, Comfrey, Shepherds Purse, with Comfrey being the most important.

AQUARIUS

The complaints of Aquarius are: Toxic blood, paralysis, eye problems, rheumatic fever. AQUARIUS HEALING HERBS ARE: Tribalene, Ragwort, Wood Sage, Blue Vervain, with Tribalene being the most important.

PISCES

The complaints of Pisces are: Painful feet and toes, gout, ulcers, boils, corns and blood impurities. PISCES HEALING HERBS ARE: Yarrow, Cayenne, Tribalene, Ginger, with Yarrow being the most important.

Are Herbs Hygienic?

As most people know, I was drinking an herbal formula every day while recovering from terminal cancer. I continued to drink the formula by the gallon. Its taste wasn't that bad.

After full recovery, I had the privilege of meeting Britain's herbalist expert who really taught me a lot about herbs. It seems that if you are able to go into the country and pick your own herbs, take them home and clean them with fresh water, all is fine. But most people buy their herbs from a store and this is where the trouble starts because the herbs could have been picked last year and maybe sat in a warehouse for six months before packaging, then mixed into tea and have been sitting on a shelf at the store ever since.

Most of the goodness has gone. It was this that started an investigation on just how to prepare herbs so that the goodness of the herbs remains. We left this problem for our scientists to figure out while I went to Denmark to watch a crop of red clover cut and gathered by a farmer. My combination of herbs are cleaned and sifted three times, not once like other companies, then subjected to a special purifying treatment that eliminates everything but leaves the goodness intact. It is ground up at temperatures below freezing and placed in a capsule or shaker to be spread on food. We have been told by the herb people in California that this system is the cleanest and safest way to prepare herbs and other large companies have already started offering to purchase the system so that they can present a better product also.

Chapter 18
The Reason

The London taxi driver dropped me off outside a four-story terrace house that had seen better days. I paid him and he quickly drove off. The sign on the door read, "SCIENTIFIC RESEARCH FORTHE PREVENTION OF DISEASE." It was on the fourth floor and, with no elevator, it was quite a climb. The office was small, and was equipped with a very old lady and a very new computer. I had no appointment and had decided to give my name as Mr. Goodman, just in case they had heard of me. I wanted to test them fully.

Mrs. Higgins didn't even look at me as she started her running commentary which seemed to bore even her. "We at the center give each person certain forms containing 152 questions. You must answer them absolutely truthfully or it's a waste of our time and yours. When you have completed the questionnaires you must send them back to this office with a check in the amount of twenty pounds

"We put your answers into the computer and they are analyzed. In due time you will receive a complete summary of the illnesses you are prone to, the ones you must watch out for. The computer will know this from the kind of stress you have been subjected to, the emotional side, and also the type of childhood that you have had. Thank you and good-bye Mr. Goodman!"

I found myself out on the street within five minutes of my arrival and I had not had the chance to ask even one of the thousand questions that I had planned to. To make matters worse, I had to walk about two miles before I could hail a cab. While I walked I found I kept muttering to myself, "that woman was enough to give anyone stress, talk about computers taking over," and on and on I complained.

Once back at the Grosvenor House Hotel I read the forms, which were both difficult yet simple. Simple questions, but they raked up a lot of very unhappy memories for me. It took me over five hours to answer the 152 questions honestly and the next morning I sent the forms back to Mrs. Higgins along with the check. None of the questions were about illness or about previous health problems.

In three weeks, the dreaded report came. It was exactly as follows.

REPORT 6303.
JASON GOODMAN (WINTERS) LONDON FILE

Born as the third child to a very unhappy couple. Father asthmatic, mother neurotic, having many affairs. Subject was the result of one such union with a neighbor. Mother would tell her friends how hard she had tried to terminate the pregnancy and this in front of the child. Mother would call the subject a freak because he was well over six feet tall at 14 years of age.

Both the subject's sisters had great animosity toward subject, with no affection whatsoever. Mother told subject constantly that he was not as good as the others. He was also expected to fail. Sisters also found it impossible to give love and affection.

Subject grew up in an atmosphere of selfishness, bitterness and hatred, with no love, compassion or even interest for his future.

Subject had a most unhappy childhood and is typical of a future cancer victim. Out of the 6,500 cases studied so far, an astounding 78 percent had similar unhappy backgrounds and most developed cancer.

Subject should be wary of nose, throat, tongue and mouth problems, including cancer.

I had already suffered terminal cancer of the tongue, jaw bone, tonsils and mouth, but they did not know that. I thought that this was remarkable.

I could not help remembering that when I did come down

with terminal cancer, my sister was two blocks away, but she would not come to see me. She has also never congratulated me regarding beating cancer, and has chosen never to mention my top-selling book, or the work we are doing worldwide. A close source has said that she would have rather I had died than become successful.

Because of this, may I urge all parents to please give openly of their love. Don't be afraid to show affection, hug your kids regularly. If parents only realized the importance of raising children, of telling them that they are good, nice, sweet, and that you love them, they would do it all the time.

Problems Are Illusions

The old man frightened me because he was so old and was obviously dying. The wood fire burned merrily in the corner of the old cabin. I tried to smile but he saw the tears in my eyes. "Do not cry for me my son, for even in one million years we will both still be in existence."

We worry so much about nothing that we make ourselves sick. When we are not worrying, we worry about why we are not worrying. But it's as all religions tell us, it is all an illusion.

For instance, you are not short of money, just short of ideas, because money rushes to ideas.

You are not unemployed, you are just trained for the wrong job

You don't disagree with your spouse, you just don't know how to communicate.

You are not terminal, you just don't know about eternal life.

You must get up and get going, for not even God can steer a parked car.

It is said that a lifetime of tragedy and Sorrow is forgotten in a second, once you gaze on the face of Jesus.

All you have to do is furnish the sinner, He will furnish the saviour. Even the blind beggar sitting on the road to Jericho knew the secret and was healed, so don't despair, your faith will set you free.

Shackled with a heavy burden full of sin and shame
and suddenly He touched me and
I will never be the Same.

Portrait Of Christ

About 2,000 years ago a Roman named Publius Lentulus wrote a report to his emperor Tiberius and included the following description of the man known as Jesus Christ. "A tall, well-proportioned man, his hair is the color of new wine...curled as it falls to (his shoulders). Upon the forehead, it parts in two. His forehead is flat and fair, his face without blemish or defect and adorned with a graceful expression. His nose and mouth are very well proportioned; his beard thick and the color of his hair, red gold. His eyes are gray and extremely lively. He is the handsomest man in the world."

—*The report is kept in the Archives in Rome.*

Summation And Beliefs

I do not believe that the herbs mentioned in this book cure illnesses or disease. I think that they do one thing and that is to purify the blood. Once this is done then the immune system can start to work to heal your own body. Your body actually heals itself.

God in His wisdom put a special herb on each continent to do just one thing, purify a person's blood. Knowing full well that when this was done, a person's body would heal itself. In Biblical times, before fluoride in the water, polluted air, and processed food, one of these herbs would have worked, but not today. Our blood is so toxic that it takes the combined efforts of the three herbs from the three continents to really work well. This is what the author did by accident many years ago.

There is no person or company associated with Jason Winters that believes any other than the above.

Every religion since the beginning of time emphasizes the importance of the blood. That's what is really meant by "the blood of Christ," the saying "life is in the blood" and "purify your blood with herbs and all things fall away." God did not just throw us down here and say "there is a polluted world with 10,000 fast food restaurants, go to it!" He gave us an immune system, all we need to do is to help it out a little.

It's no accident that the Aborigines, Africans, Indians, Arabs, Chinese, Tibetans all purify their blood on a daily basis. We in North America do not, and our sickness and death rate is the highest it has ever been.

One Reason Why

A Tibetan wakes in the morning, stretches, yawns, looks out at the sun and smiles. He thanks God that he is alive and fully expects a long, happy life and a very good day and so that's what he gets.

We in the west wake up and turn on television. A top star is telling us that if we get sick at our age, it's going to wipe us out financially. Our medical coverage just isn't enough, we must pay for more. We turn the channel in disgust to hear a man shouting, "buy your burial plot today, don't leave it to your children!!" One more channel change brings on a doctor telling us to "look for lumps in the breasts each day, check for moles that are changing, rush to your doctor, check your blood pressure at the supermarket." Thoroughly depressed, we pour white sugar and cream all over our crispy crunchy cereal, wash it down with three cups of black coffee, light up a cigarette and cough and wheeze all the way to the office where we must perform well every day for our boss, or he will hire someone younger to take our place for less money. It doesn't matter how well you did last year or even last week, you must perform well today or else!

Is this really what God wanted for you, His perfect creation? No, of course not, but there is a way out, as millions have found, for that one little sentence can change your life, yes "life is in the blood."

Book Three

Breakthrough: In Search Of The Australian Legend

What a piece of work is man!
How noble in reason! How infinite in faculties!
In form and moving, how express and admirable!
In action, how like an angel!
In apprehension, how like a god!

Excerpt from Hamlet, Act II
by William Shakespeare *(1564 - 1616)*
taken from Complete Collective Works of Shakespeare,
published 1861 by Johnson & Frye

Chapter 19

The Miracle Healing Of the Ages

Aborigine

The man was running as fast as he could, but still the strange looking animal was catching up with him. Wide-eyed, snarling and with saliva streaking from its mouth, the mad "thing" was a terrifying sight. It was about 700 yards behind its prey, a small Bundjalung aborigine. The man's breath came in agonizing bursts and extreme fright had given his legs great strength. But still the animal gained ground. It was grassy with not too many trees, the closest being about one-quarter of a mile away. That was the only thing the man could see. He must get to that tree before the "thing" caught up with him.

Sweat poured from his body, his bare feet were cut and bleeding badly. His gasping for breath became even more strangled. It was the year 1610, near the coast of Northeastern Australia, a time and place where only the toughest survived.

At last he was within reach of the tree. He had to jump high to reach the lowest branch and he screamed with pain when the animal, at last catching up with him, managed to take a bite out of his heel.

The animal stayed at the base of the tree for about 12 hours before, very discouraged, it left the area. After a considerable wait, the man came down from the tree and started on his long trek home to his village. He did not limp, nor was he in any pain from his cut feet and bitten heel.

The tree he had taken refuge in was a very special tree, which the natives of that era called the "healing tree." It is a fairly fragile tree. Especially this one and the man was thankful that he was so small and lightweight. While he had been waiting in the tree he had been busy.

First he would take a leaf and rub it into his wounds. Then he would gather some larger leaves and wrap his feet entirely. Soon the pain was gone. And he knew that healing had begun.

This, then is the first real story of the amazing Melaleuca tree. The healing tree, or as the world now knows it...the tea tree

INTRODUCTION

When white settlers began to arrive in Australia, they at first made war on the Aborigines they found there. As the white men at last developed the wisdom to try to understand and appreciate the native people of this extraordinary land, they discovered there was much to learn from them

One of the great secrets imparted to them by the aborigines was of the healing powers of a precious oil contained in tiny sacs on the leaves of certain trees that grew in the swampy forests. This tree became known as the Tea Tree. Its oil had great curative and antiseptic properties, yet was seemingly without ill side-effects of any kind and was a great boon to the people living in those dangerous times.

Unfortunately, in Western man's rush to prove that he can do better than God, synthetic medications came into vogue as the only respected ones and Tea Tree Oil was largely forgotten by the civilized Western World.

In 1984, Jason Winters (he is now Sir Jason, having shortly thereafter received a knighthood for his outstanding contributions to humanity in the field of health) learned of this oil from the aborigines while visiting Australia on a speaking tour. He was so impressed with what he heard that he launched into an investigation of its powers.

The following is Sir Jason's own account of the miraculous properties of this wonderful, natural healing oil, based on his own research.

The Australian Legend

The plane touched the ground with a teeth jarring thud, bounced along the runway and at last came to a stop before the Quantas Airline terminal. I stretched my legs gratefully. The long journey from Los Angeles to Sydney was over.

I have always loved Australia and considered it one of the most beautiful and fascinating lands I have visited, so it was a great pleasure to have been invited there to speak on a number of radio shows—well worth the 24-hour flight. This was my third tour of the country (arranged by my publisher), and I had shows to do in Sydney, Brisbane, Melbourne, Adelaide and Perth. It would be a quick and very busy six days, then home again.

Next day, feeling bright and energetic, I tackled the biggest radio show in Australia, the "N.S.W. Talk Back" show. As usual, I was answering innumerable calls regarding my first book, "Killing Cancer," when I received a rather unusual call.

This was from a man with a strange voice, a sort of accent I'd never heard before. He said he was a native of Australia and that he had been told that I was interested in the healing power of herbs. I said, "Yes, that's true." He then told me of a miraculous substance called Tea Tree Oil and began relating stories of its wonderful curative powers.

I was fascinated and we talked on and on, though numerous other callers were waiting.

Finally, the announcer signaled me frantically that I must terminate that conversation and move on to other calls. I did so, arranging to meet my intriguing caller later in the day.

As I took the remaining waiting calls and answered the questions of the good people wanting to talk with me, the thought of this Tea Tree Oil lingered in the back of my mind. I couldn't escape the feeling that something important was about to happen.

When the show was over, I went quickly to the lobby. A small, dark-skinned man rose from his chair and approached me, announcing that he was my mysterious caller. His name was Joe Culvong, he said. He was an aborigine, a true native of Australia.

He told me more about the miraculous tree that grows in his native bush country and of the healing powers of its precious oil. My feeling of excitement grew. If even only one-quarter of what he said was true, the world deserved to know of the wonderful properties of this natural substance. I decided to go with him to his home in New South Wales where his tribe lived to see for myself.

We made the long journey from Sydney by car. His people lived in miserable conditions, for they have been badly taken advantage of by the whites, far worse than the American Indians. However, they are by nature proud, strong and agile, and have a great knowledge of natural remedies.

We two looked quite the pair as we traveled about: I, tall, grey and obviously an outlander, he about half my size, nut-colored and very much at home wherever we went. But we got along famously, and I learned a great deal from this wonderful man. It is because of him that this book is being written and I owe him a debt of gratitude for letting me know about this miraculous substance. Naturally, I procured some Tea Tree Oil for myself and soon vowed that I would never be without it again.

Wherever we went people gladly gathered round us, and I heard many gratifying stories of the uses of Tea Tree Oil. One man told me of infected, pus-filled wounds that had been cleansed and healed by the miracle oil of this tree. Another related how a lingering fungus infection (which so often plagues people living in damp climates) had been eradicated. Some of the women told me shyly of female problems that had been cured promptly and of the use of Tea Tree Oil in healing severe burns.

Many mentioned the dreaded coral cuts from the reefs along the Australian coast, which are so dangerous because they easily become infected and spread poison throughout the whole body, yet when Tea Tree Oil was spread on them, immediately the cuts healed cleanly.

The stories went on and on: Headaches were stopped by placing a drop of oil on the temples, which also cleared the sight of tired eyes. Arthritis pain was eased by rubbing the oil on the affected joints, muscle aches and pains responded to this treatment as well.

I heard how Tea Tree Oil was used effectively to treat boils, cysts, insect bites, warts, impetigo, cases of lice infestation and various infections, yet had also proved effective in treatment of severe burns and terrible vaginal itching.

A germicidal substance strong enough to penetrate pus and cleanse septic wounds, yet gentle enough to be used as a healing agent on the most delicate tissues? This certainly warranted further study. How could it be that the whole world didn't know of this miraculous substance? I vowed to find out all I could about this wonderful gift of nature and to share that knowledge with others.

Nature's Miracle Healer

The Tea Tree-Melaleuca alternifolia-is a beautiful and rare plant that grows only in Australia. It is said that it derived its name from Captain Cook's sailors, who brewed a spicy and refreshing tea from its leaves, and the name remained over the succeeding centuries.

The Bundjalung aborigines had lived among the ancient Tea Trees for thousands of years and had learned of the medicinal value of the precious oil that came from the leaves of these remarkable trees. From early times to the present, legend abounds with stories of the healing effected by Tea Tree Oil—healings that present-day medicine would be hard pressed to duplicate with a wide range of "wonder drugs," much less a single substance.

Behind all legend is at least a grain of truth. I set out to discover if the truth could really be as wonderful as legend said it was and discovered it was even more so.

Since Australia is the only source of Tea Tree Oil, it seemed logical to begin by researching all available literature there for documented evidence that Tea Tree Oil really had the remarkable properties attributed to it. Upon investigation I found that not only does aboriginal folklore extol the virtues of Tea Tree Oil, but that physicians in general practice, gynecologists, surgeons, naturopaths, dentists and chemists have all praised its wonderful results as well.

As early as the 1920s, laboratory experiments were conducted in Australia to scientifically determine the properties of Tea Tree Oil. A respected government chemist in New South Wales named A.R. Penfeld, who was also curator and economic chemist of the Technological Museum in Sydney, reported very favorably on the antiseptic properties of the Tea Tree Oil. One of the qualities of the oil that he mentioned in a report before the Royal Society of New South Wales was that Tea Tree Oil was 13 times stronger as an antiseptic than carbolic acid, which was the universal standard of that time.

Later research led to a report in the Medical Journal of Australia that pleasing results had been obtained in actual general practice of medicine by applying Tea Tree Oil to septic wounds, carbuncles and pus-filled infections. The editor of this journal stated that the results obtained were most encouraging, and a striking feature of the oil was that it dissolved the pus and left the surface of infected wounds clean so that its germicidal action became more effective without any apparent damage to the tissues. This was especially impressive since the presence of pus usually renders other antiseptics ineffective or virtually useless

In the 1930s, the British Medical Journal also stated that Tea Tree Oil was a powerful disinfectant that had been used successfully in a very wide range of septic conditions, and that it was both nonpoisonous and non-irritant.

Tea Tree Oil came to be used successfully in dental treatment of pyorrhea, gingivitis, nerve capping and hemorrhaging, for gynecological problems and for disinfecting and healing wounds. What made it unique from other antiseptics was that the oil was found to be most effective in dirty or pus-laden conditions. It was also found to have remarkable healing effects in a broad spectrum of skin fungi, including tinea, candida and paronychia.

This information is to be found in such respected publications as the "Medical Journal of Australia," the "British Medical Journal," the "Australian Journal of Pharmacy," and the "Journal of the National Medical Association" of the U.S.A.

An article in the Australian publication "Nature and Health" reports that a physidan of the Southern Cross Herbal College of New South Wales has been using Tea Tree Oil as the primary treatment of vaginitis, cystitis, urethritis and fungal infections and notes that the oil can be taken orally and used as a topical application, both with consistent success.

The same article reports that a Swiss firm has used Tea Tree Oil for more than 30 years in the treatment of monilia. This article also stated that four types of chronic vaginal infections have been cured by douching with Tea Tree Oil in a dilution of four parts Tea Tree Oil to 1,000 parts water. It cites a report in the "Obstetrics and Gynecology Journal" that a controlled study of 130 women confirmed that the oil of the Australian Melaleuca alternifolia (Tea Tree Oil) in suitable dilutions was found to be highly effective in treatment of trichomonal vaginitis, moniliasis, cervicitis and chronic endocervicitis. A report on the oil's uses published by Australian Essential Oil Ltd. in Sydney included treatment of pyorrhea and diabetic gangrene.

I even learned the interesting fact that during World War II this medicinal oil was added to machine cutting oils in factories since its germicidal and healing properties reduced infection from skin injuries to a minimum, especially infections resulting from abrasions to the hands from metal filings and turnings. The oil was widely used for this purpose in ammunition annexes.

Perhaps the most astonishing thing is that Tea Tree Oil can be used both internally and externally-and this despite its incredible strength as a germicide and antiseptic. It is also extremely gentle to wounded or delicate tissues in the process of healing.

Tea Tree Oil's use in limiting the scarring and secondary infections caused by burns is extraordinary. On the other hand, it is also excellent as an additive to skin cleansers and scalp lotions and shampoos because of its powerful solvent action. It can even be used as a mange treatment for dogs, cats and horses, since it is extremely effective in healing skin problems. Researchers are now evaluating its effectiveness in the treatment of herpes.

By the late 1930s, Tea Tree Oil was being used not only as a bush remedy, but in orthodox medicine as well. It was also found to be an ideal household disinfectant, since it is many times stronger than other disinfectants commonly used in the home, yet is safer, more versatile in its uses and kinder to the skin. There is also great value to be placed on the fact that it is nonpoisonous, which makes it even more desirable in homes with small children.

What a shame that such a miraculous oil should have fallen from widespread use and its benefits been denied to the general public! Much of the early research was soon forgotten in favor of synthetic germicides and "wonder drugs," which were developed around the time of World War II.

One of the problems, of course, was that it is so difficult to harvest the precious oil from the Tea Tree that producing it didn't offer the vast financial rewards that the drug companies manufacturing synthetic medicines could experience. The high profits these man-made drugs produced enabled the drug companies to promote the use of their synthetics worldwide.

Tea Tree Oil, on the other hand, must be painstakingly harvested and distilled in much the same way it was done for thousands of years by the aborigines. Melaleuca alternifolia—the Tea Tree—grows best in wet, swampy areas that have defied man's mechanical harvesting. Even today the leaves of the Tea Tree are stripped from the trees by hand. This has its good side, however, since harvesting the leaves for oil does not destroy or damage the trees in any way. They simply send out new leaves and shoots each year and continue growing larger and stronger.

When you realize that it requires about a ton of Tea Tree leaves to produce only 10 liters of the tree's miraculous oil, you understand more clearly how precious this rare substance really is. However, since it is so concentrated, a small bottle of the oil seems to last indefinitely.

It is in no way my mission to set up Tea Tree Oil as a cure-all for everything that ails humanity. However, I couldn't help but be impressed with all I had learned. The personal experiences of thousands of people coupled with overwhelming scientific evidence clearly demonstrated to me that Tea Tree Oil has remarkable and versatile healing powers.

I am constantly surprised that some skeptics tend to consider any natural healing substance as too good to be true, yet they will put complete faith in man-made drugs. I, on the other hand, having overcome terminal cancer with the help of natural herbs when I had been written off as a hopeless case by the traditional medical profession, have ample reason to believe in God and in God-given means of healing. I would never question God's ability to provide mankind with such a beneficent and natural healer as Tea Tree Oil, and I want to share what I have learned about it with others so that they might benefit from it as so many have already done.

The Search For The True Healing Oil

Once convinced of the very real virtue of Tea Tree Oil, I wanted to learn more about where this remarkable substance comes from and why it is so effective a healer. Also, I wanted to determine if all oils from the Tea Tree are alike. I discovered that they most definitely are not.

As stated before, the Tea Tree grows only in Australia. There are some 300 varieties of the tree, but only one type, the Melaleuca alternifolia, is known to produce medicinal oil with the healing properties we have spoken of. Moreover, only trees grown in certain regions and under the proper conditions provide oil with the most desirable qualities.

The oil of the Melaleuca alternifolia—Tea Tree Oil—is an extremely complex substance. It is known to contain at least 48 organic compounds. They are found together only in this miraculous oil—a true gift of nature. It is interesting to note that none of these 48 compounds is particularly effective alone. It is apparently the synergy of the intricate combination—the way they work naturally together—that produces their unique healing power.

One very important thing that I learned is that there is a wide divergence in the quality of various Tea Tree oils, that some inferior types of the oil are not only ineffective, but can actually be irritating to the skin and other tissues. Trees that look exactly alike, may produce oils of very different quality. A factor that greatly affects the properties of Tea Tree Oil is its content of the two compounds terpinin 4-ol and cineole. Terpinin-4-ol is a highly desirable ingredient that contributes to Tea Tree Oil's healing properties, and to be effective a quality oil must have a high content of it. Cineole, on the contrary, is an undesirable compound, and a high percentage of it in the oil can cause irritation rather than healing. Two oils can look and smell the same, yet be of very different quality. I cannot emphasize enough the importance of using only high quality Tea Tree Oil.

I have heard that many producers aren't aware of these natural differences in the quality of the oil and quite innocently market poor quality oil, while some others are unscrupulous enough not to care as long as they can make a profit from it.

The highest quality oil comes from a very small region in Australia and is not always easy to come by. So I began to search for a reliable source that I could tell people about. A revised edition of my book "Cleanse," including the chapter on Tea Tree Oil, was about to be printed and I wanted to let people who were interested in or had a need for Tea Tree Oil know more about how they could get quality oil.

CHAPTER 20

PERSONAL STORIES FROM USERS OF TEA TREE OIL

Since the publication of "Cleanse," I have heard from hundreds of people who have contacted me to thank me for telling them about Tea Tree Oil or to tell me other stories of remarkable healings that have come about through its use. People have written just raving about this discovery.

Space doesn't permit me to include all of their stories, but I would like to share with you just a few of them. I am omitting the most dramatic ones, such as the one that accompanied the photos I received of a woman whose leg was so diseased with diabetic gangrene that surgeons were determined to amputate it. Later photos showed the same leg—miraculously improved and well on the way to healing after the use of Tea Tree Oil.

Some people have said to me, "Jason, people don't read natural health books," yet over 3,000,000 copies of my book "Killing Cancer" have already been sold and "Cleanse" is now well on its way to surpassing that number.

People ARE reading health books, but some of them are afraid to admit it, because in America if something is not prescribed by a doctor or manufactured by a large chemical company, it is considered unprofessional. Natural cures, such as those spoken of in the Bible-are not only suspect, they are often illegal, despite the fact that they save the health and even the lives of thousands of people every year. I have said before that if Jesus were to walk among us today he would be arrested for practicing medicine without a license.

I am determined to share with the readers of my books the great secrets of nature that I have learned, though I almost died of cancer before I got around to learning them.

Following are some of the wonderful stories people have shared with me.

What A Dentist Has To Say About Tea Tree Oil

A forward-thinking American dentist recently described how he used Tea Tree Oil in his dental practice. He had been attracted to it for its versatility and remarkable properties in treating a variety of problems and had found that it kills resistant bacteria within 20 seconds after direct contact and is also an excellent fungicide. He considers it especially remarkable in that Tea Tree Oil will penetrate into tissues and also has anesthetic properties. It actually seems to control discomfort without causing numbness.

This dentist reported using Tea Tree Oil to successfully treat patients with a wide variety of difficulties. One patient had a denture sore in his mouth that the dentist described as "awesome looking." This patient put Tea Tree Oil on the sore two to three times daily and the sore healed quickly and without scarring. The dentist described this healing as nothing short of "incredible.

He has also used Tea Tree Oil to stop pain when he was working on a patient with deep decay in a tooth. The patient reported that the tooth stopped hurting immediately after the Tea Tree Oil had been put into the cavity and had no postoperative discomfort.

The dentist also reports having treated canker sores by applying Tea Tree Oil full strength to the sore. After only one to two applications the pain was gone and the sores went into remission. He also treated strep throat-the most painful of sore throats-with two drops of Tea Tree Oil in two ounces of water. Two or three rinsings of this solution and the sore throats were gone. He also used Tea Tree Oil full strength while doing root canals and found it seemed to penetrate and soften dentin.

One of his patients needed root canal therapy, but the affected tooth was too sensitive from a "hot" abscess to achieve adequate anesthesia. The dentist placed a cotton pellet saturated with Tea Tree Oil over the soft dentin and seated it in.

When the patient returned a week later, local anesthesia worked well.

The dentist also reveals that he has seen purulent fistulas which he treated by saturating a paper point with Tea Tree Oil and placing it in the fistulous tract. Within seven days there was no evidence of any previous problem. He also notes having seen "near miraculous results" in the treatment of both chronic and acute periodontal problems. He considers this experimental, but has gotten impressive results with the use of Tea Tree Oil. One method was to use two drops of oil diluted with two ounces of water as wash or one drop of oil used with toothpaste for brushing. He has also placed the Tea Tree Oil directly into a periodontal abscess with excellent results.

These reported results are impressive indeed and come from a very professional source. Since even the FDA considers Tea Tree Oil "a natural antiseptic fungicide," it seems likely that this wonderful natural product wilt soon be universally recognized as a God-given boon to mankind.

Fungus Infections

"It was like a miracle! I could scarcely believe my eyes!" So said a woman in San Diego who had suffered with a severe fungus infection of the fingernails and toenails. This condition had persisted for four years and had responded only slightly to traditional treatment. The woman had seen four dermatologists who had treated her, but though the fungus would get somewhat better from time to time, it would flare up again and had become worse than ever.

It was not only unsightly, but painful, since a large portion of the toenails on her big toes had become affected and had to be cut back to permit treatment. This left much of the nail bed exposed and extremely tender. Wearing shoes was often painful and this woman had almost despaired of ever finding an effective treatment of the condition. Through my book she learned of Tea Tree Oil's use as a fungicide and decided to try it, more or less as a last resort.

"The first time I applied it the discomfort and inflammation in my toes subsided," the woman told me. "I was pleasantly surprised and you can imagine how delighted I was when within a very short time the fungus seemed to be completely gone and my nails started growing in again, healthy and strong. I am very grateful that I was able to obtain a supply of Tea Tree Oil and I don't intend to ever be without it again. I've also found that it makes an excellent disinfectant for cuts and abrasions since it doesn't sting and cause pain as some other treatments do. I'm using it as a household disinfectant for cleaning, too, because I've learned from your book what an effective germicide it is. I even like the way it smells."

Another case of fungus infection on the hands of a young boy was mentioned in "Cleanse." The usual medications had failed to alleviate this boy's bad fungus infection, yet it responded remarkably after only one week of application of Tea Tree Oil. This occurred in a modern clinic in the Boston, Massachusetts, area. The attending physician reported that this boy's hands became like velvet in one week. The same physician is now trying Tea Tree Oil in the treatment of other conditions.

One man contacted me to tell me about an article in an Australian magazine that told the story of a woman who had suffered a painful and disfiguring rash on her legs for six years. She had tried prescription medications she could ill afford, but to no avail. In fact, many of these prescriptions seriously worsened her condition. She began to use Tea Tree Oil and two weeks after she first applied it, her intractable skin fungus cleared up. (This story appeared in the Australian publication "Nature and Health.")

I was also sent photographs of the hands of a young man of 15 who for seven years had a severe skin problem that doctors seemed to be unable to identify. The young man had consulted three different dermatologists as well as an acupuncturist and his own pediatrician. (The condition occurred when the boy was only eight.) By this time over $6,000 had been spent on treatment for his condition, yet nothing these doctors were able to prescribe cleared up the young man's skin problem. After using pure Tea Tree Oil for only 10 days his condition had improved dramatically. After a month the difference was phenomenal.

The Eldon Lowder Story

It came as a big surprise to me when upon opening a letter from Australia I noticed that it mentioned the name Eldon Lowder. As readers of my previous book, "Killing Cancer," might remember Eldon is a man living in the state of Utah in the United States of America who manufactures a special colonic board that allows people to give themselves colonics right in their own homes. A colonic is a process in which a person allows a steady stream of water to enter the colon, breaking away debris and rotting fecal matter. The special board Eldon Lowder designed for this purpose has since been put into use around the world.

I use this board constantly ever since the British Medical Association put out that special paper stating that death begins in the colon. They found that the colon, being dark, warm and moist, breeds bacteria that causes an enormous amount of illness and some doctors went so far as to say that it is impossible to get well or even to enjoy mediocre health while the colon is so dirty.

The woman who wrote me from Australia had purchased one of the special Lowder Boards and just raved about it. "However, she said, and I quote, "three months ago I started adding 10 drops of a liquid called Tea Tree Oil to every colonic I took. The results have been astounding. This has the effect of purifying the lower bowel and colon, and I know that it kills bacteria because I read about it in our local newspaper."

She continued, "Thank you again for telling me in your first book about the Lowder Colonic Board. It has changed my life. This letter is my chance to repay you, for I know that if you inform Mr. Lowder about the Tea Tree Oil, he will be in a position to tell the world about using it in the colonic cleanse and in this way will help thousands of people."

I did contact Eldon Lowder about this and he was thrilled. Also, I started on the colonic Tea Tree Oil myself and noticed a big difference the first day.

I feel sure that there will come a time when all colonic therapists will be using Tea Tree Oil.

The Aaron Ongman Story

Although Aaron was only one year old, he had suffered quite a lot from diaper rash. Even when his mother used disposable diapers the rash still persisted.

She had tried just about every type of cream and powder, but to no avail. Then she heard about Tea Tree Oil, obtained a bottle from a lady in Hawaii and started using it.

"I would put 10 drops of Tea Tree Oil into a glass of warm water and just spread it on the affected area. Lo and behold, the rash was gone in three days and has not returned.

I also heard that a child down the street managed to rid herself of acne (pimples on the face) with only a few applications. Thank you so much for telling people about this. It smells so good too.

I now put six or seven drops into the washing machine during a wash and the clothes smell so fresh.

The Amazing Story Of The Arctic Adventurer

Wonderful experiences with Tea Tree Oil certainly aren't limited to any one part of the world these days. I was even told of one amazing story about a man living in Arctic Red River in the Northwest Territories of Canada. While traveling from one community to another, this man lost all of his supplies, even his matches, to marauding animals. That night the temperature got down to 30 degrees below zero and the man was very close to freezing to death.

He had his dog with him and to keep his hands from freezing, the traveler cut his dog open and put his hands inside its stomach to thaw them out.

Because of the extreme cold the dog didn't bleed heavily and, when this man's hands thawed out sufficiently to be usable, he got a needle and thread from his pocket, sewed the dog's stomach back up and poured Tea Tree Oil on the incision. The dog lived and was perfectly well afterward.

(From the December issue of "Northern Lights.")

Notes

Chapter 21

Other Treatments and Uses

Vaginal Infection And Itching

I constantly hear from women just raving about how effective Tea Tree Oil is in treating vaginal infections. Some of them have been under treatment of one sort or another for years without results, yet when they start the Tea Tree Oil their problems clear up right away. For some reason these vaginal infections are very resistant to treatment, the organisms that cause them being very hardy indeed. But even chronic cases seem to respond to treatment with Tea Tree Oil.

Since nature has not equipped me to experience these results personally, I'll just have to take the word of these wonderful ladies who take the time to share the good news with the rest of us. There is some medical literature on the subject I can share with you however.

A study was done by a Dr. Eduardo Pena with the purpose of determining the value and safety of using the oil as a vaginal douche and for topical application in the treatment of trichomonal vaginitis, Candida albicans vaginitis and other vaginal infections. The doctor also wanted to determine any possible side-effects and the proper strength of the oil for utmost safety and efficiency

As the basic medication, Dr. Pena used an emulsified 40 percent solution of Australian Melaleuca alternifolia oil (Tea Tree Oil) with isopropyl alcohol 13 percent. Various dilutions of this medication were made as described.

Dr. Pena reported that he started his project with 10 patients with chronic cervicitis, treating them with full strength medication (as described above) in the form of saturated tampons made with four-by-four-inch sponges left in the vagina. After thoroughly washing the perineum, labia and vagina with pHisoHex and a thorough drying, the vaginal canal was washed with a 40 percent solution of the medication and the tampon was left in place for 24 hours.

The cervicitis was cured and healed after weekly treatments. The medication at no time irritated the vaginal mucosa, but merely had a drying effect. He found the effective concentration of treatment of cervicitis to be 50 percent of the basic medication, that is a 20 percent solution of the oil.

In the 96 cases of trichomonal vaginitis, clinical cures with restoration of the cervix to normal were obtained by the following regimen:

1. Thorough washing of the vulva and vagina with pHisoHex.
2. Drying.
3. Topical application and washing of the vagina (after drying) with a one percent solution of the basic medication, using approximately 15 cc.
4. Insertion of a saturated tampon made of three four-by-four sponges into the vagina with the patient instructed to remove same after 24 hours.
5. Daily vaginal douches of one percent of basic medication (i.e., 0.4 percent Melaleuca alternifolia oil) in one quart of water.

The total number of office treatments required to affect a clinical cure by this regimen averaged six and the total number of vaginal douches per patient averaged 42. At no time did the patient have to remove the packing or discontinue the douches because of irritation, burning or other complaints.

The aesthetic qualities of the oil are also remarked on, with patients reported as commenting on its pleasant odor and soothing effect. It was especially pleasing as a douche, since it removed obnoxious vaginal odors.

Tea Tree Oil In The Treatment Of Boils And Pimples

Tea Tree Oil has proved to be an excellent treatment for boils and festering pimples because of its unique ability to gain entrance into the affected area through the top layers of skin. It can actually penetrate unbroken skin and thus can carry its disinfecting action right down into the boil or pimple!

Most of us know how painful a boil can be.

The worst of it is, since they usually form around a sebaceous gland or a hair follicle, they frequently appear in very inconvenient spots—such as right where your shirt collar rubs the most or where it makes it uncomfortable to sit down. They are difficult to treat and tend to spread, with other boils developing in the same area from pus carried by the original boil to adjacent follicles. Lancing them has been the time-honored treatment, a painful and drastic one that often leaves scars.

I have heard of absolutely wonderful results from treating boils with Tea Tree Oil. There have been just hundreds and hundreds of cases where they have cleared up completely, and these marvelous cases are backed up by medical studies.

One such study by Dr. Henry Feinblatt reported that in 25 cases treated with the oil, only one boil required incision. In the majority of the cases the infected site of the boil was completely removed within eight days and there were no toxic effects from the treatment in any of the cases.

Here is a typical case history: A 40-year-old man had a boil on his neck at the collar line that had developed within two days. It was large, red, swollen and so painful to the touch that the patient couldn't stand the pressure of his shirt collar.

This man was also diabetic and had a previous history of recurring boils. The oil (Melaleuca alternifolia, which we know as Tea Tree Oil) was applied directly over the site of the boil two or three times daily after thoroughly cleansing the area of the boil.

Within two days there was a definite improvement. After four days most of the inflammation was gone, after eight days the skin healed over the site of the former boil. After this favorable experience, the patient repeated the use of the oil whenever he developed a new boil and in each instance was able to abort the development of further boils.

The doctor reporting this study observed that the Tea Tree Oil encouraged more rapid healing without scarring than conservative treatment in the control cases and concluded that the high germicidal activity of the oil against staphylococcus aureus accounts for the rapid improvement it brings when used in the treatment of boils. This study was written up in the Journal of the National Medical Association (U.S.A.).

First Aid With Tea Tree Oil

In the course of my travels and while speaking on various radio shows where listeners call in to talk with me, I have spoken with many physicians who, as I am, are interested in natural healing products and who are delighted to learn more about Tea Tree Oil. It has not only proved to be remarkably effective in treating major infections such as we have already described, it is also just the most wonderful product to have around the house for myriad uses that I can think of. In addition to being a safe, pure germicide and disinfectant that is many times stronger than other products, it is ideal for first aid—an entire first aid kit in a bottle.

MUSCLE ACHES—Rub pure Tea Tree Oil into muscles. Add 10 drops to hot bath and soak.

BOILS—Apply Tea Tree Oil directly three times a day.

CUTS AND ABRASIONS—Dab on pure Tea Tree Oil.

MOSQUITO BITES, STINGS, SAND FLIES—Dab on pure Tea Tree Oil.

LEECHES OR TICKS—Apply pure oil to kill animal, then dab Tea Tree Oil on bite.

NAIL INFECTION—Soak nail in pure Tea Tree Oil for five minutes and massage in twice daily until infection leaves.

MINOR VAGINAL INFECTIONS—Douche with 5 mls. of pure oil per one litre of water, shake well. Add 5 ml. to sitz-bath and splash in and around vagina. Dilute pure oil before using in the vagina. Normally a slight tingling will be felt.

ARTHRITIS—Mix three to five drops into a small amount of baby oil and massage deeply into joints.

ATHLETES FOOT—Wash and dry feet thoroughly, then apply pure oil twice per day.

SMELLY FEET—Add five to ten drops pure oil to warm water, bathe feet nightly for five minutes.

CARBUNCLES—Dab on pure oil twice daily.

SPRAINS—Rub pure oil into sprains for relief.

ITCHY SCALP—Add five drops of pure oil to shampoo

BLOCKED NOSE OR SINUSES—Use pure oil in Steam vaporizer. Rub drops around sinuses and inhale.

NASAL ULCERS—Apply pure Tea Tree Oil with cotton bud.

MOUTH ULCERS, SORE GUMS, BAD BREATH, PLAQUE—Dab on pure Tea Tree Oil or add three drops to water and use as a mouthwash twice daily.

COLD SORES—Dab on pure oil three times per day.

PIMPLES/ACNE—Dab on three times per day or add three to six drops of pure oil to warm water and rinse affected area.

SORE THROAT—Add three to six drops of pure oil to warm water and gargle or add three drops of pure oil to one-half glass of juice and sip slowly.

CONGESTION—Add pure oil to Steam vaporizer and inhale. Rub pure oil onto chest and back. Sprinkle on pillow before sleeping.

MINOR BURNS—Flush with cold water/ice pack immediately. Apply pure oil to burn.

SUNBURN—In severe cases apply pure oil. For minor cases, dilute oil with cream or baby oil.

DIAPER CLEANSER—Add 10 drops of pure Tea Tree oil to each four liters of water. Stir, then soak diapers overnight.

CRADLE CAP—Mix five drops pure Tea Tree Oil with

olive oil and rub into scalp. Leave five minutes, then wash hair. Keep away from eyes.

TROPICAL ULCERS, PLANTAR WARTS, CORAL CUTS—Dab on pure oil three times per day.

FLEAS—Add 10 drops pure oil to shampoo. Repeat as required.

ANIMAL CUTS AND ITCHES—Apply pure oil.

Naturally, if any ailment persists, you should seek proper medical advice. It is possible that the pure oil might irritate some very sensitive skins. If your skin is sensitive dilute the oil before using and discontinue use if irritation persists.

We are also told that Tea Tree Oil makes a marvelous difference when added to your skin creams and lotions. Its bactericidal action helps clear up skin problems and keep the skin fresh and healthy. Shampoo with Tea Tree Oil added is wonderful for clearing up itchy scalp and minor infections and helps keep your scalp and hair in tip-top condition.

In conclusion I'd like to share with you some information directly from the report of A.R. Penfold, the Australian chemist whose study gave him an enthusiastic appreciation of the marvelous benefits of Tea Tree Oil.

He said, "Although the germicidal value is high, the oil is nontoxic and nonirritating. Some idea of the wide field of usefulness in which this oil has found application can be gauged from the following conditions which have responded to treatment: Perionychia, emphysema, gynecological conditions (acute nasopharyngitis, catarrh, thrush and aphthous stomatitis, tonsillitis and ulcers of the mouth, sore throat), pyorrhea, gingivitis, etc."

He gave a few outstanding examples of the use of this oil in actual practice.

A medical man in the U.S.A. reported the successful treatment of a nasty head wound which, because of the hair, was disinclined to heal. The oil brought about a quick and healthy healing.

The Surgeon-Lieutenant of H.M.S. Sussex stationed in Egypt reported that the tinea which had broken out among the ship's company was quickly cured by an application of the oil.

Many cases of extreme ulcerations of the legs, with considerable suppurations which had not responded to treatment by any other means were quickly cured by treatment with the oil.

Even a case of successful treatment of diabetic gangrene was reported.

This information is extracted from the *Australian Journal of Pharmacy*."

Penfold remarked on his study as follows:

> "It must be emphasized that the result of these investigations not only exceeded expectations, but yielded results in practice far beyond anything that would have been anticipated from the laboratory determination."

What he's saying, of course, is that it's all very well for something to test out well in a laboratory, but what really counts is 'how well it performs in actually helping people with their very real health problems. The Tea Tree Oil worked even better than anyone would have guessed, except for the aborigines, who probably could have told them so all along.

I have spent the last 10 years of my life searching for natural means of restoring and preserving good health and I can honestly say that Tea Tree Oil is one of the most exciting products I have discovered. Just be sure to get pure Tea Tree Oil of the highest quality and you'll see for yourself why I consider Tea Tree Oil to be a miraculous breakthrough in natural healing.

Hair Straightening Technique Made Less Painful

The beautiful black girl sank into the hot bath to soothe her nerves and she started to cry. She had blisters on her forehead and ears that were most painful.

It comes as a great surprise to many people when they

find out that when white ladies get their hair permed, it is to make it curly or wavy.

The black community, however, is opposite to that. They get a perm to have their hair straightened. Some of the most beautiful ladies on television or in the movies are, as you know, black with long, luxurious, wavy hair.

While black girls look very beautiful with straight hair, they really have to suffer to obtain that result. The hair salon they choose must really know what they are doing for the chemicals involved can, and do quite often, burn the skin.

If just a little solution gets onto the skin of the forehead, or ears, the lady gets a bad burn. On the odd occasion the pain of the next few days can actually make them cry and sometimes infection of the scalp sets in.

Many of these ladies have started rinsing their hair and scalp the next day with a solution of warm water and 20 drops of Tea Tree Oil. The results are very quick and eliminate the risk of infection. Try this also to eliminate dandruff, itching and greasy-feeling hair, it works wonders.

Book Four

The Ultimate Combination

Chapter 22

After 26,000 Years It Just Happened

By Lord Stafford

World famous author Ruth Montgomery wrote about Jason Winters and his herbal tea in the first chapter of her book, "Threshold to Tomorrow."

Ruth Montgomery had mentioned at the end of the chapter that her guides had told her "Jason Winters will soon develop another process with equally startling results, for his farseeing mind and dedication to helping others will make itself felt in the years ahead."

The first formula has been used by over 62 million people and shows no signs of slowing down.

Going on the assumption that God placed an herb on earth to take care of every illness, and going on the assumption that God wants us healthy, Jason started a worldwide search for these herbs. For the past four years his friends and family have chided him for travelling too much, and never relaxing at home. As a matter of fact, he has travelled the world at least four times each year, following up stories about healing with herbs in some of the world's most remote areas.

A small laboratory in Scotland would receive the herbs that Jason sent from each country and would break them down to find their ingredients, strength, power, toxicity and value. For every 50 packages he would send them, only one would prove worthwhile.

He was looking for a group of herbs that was compatible, easily available, and ones that in combination would act against most diseases. At least one herb would have to be a proven brain food, for Jason was well aware of how mental problems often manifest themselves as physical illness.

But the most important thing was that he must stick with

the herbs that had already been approved and accepted by the Food and Drug Administration and government agencies around the world.

What good would it do to come up with a marvelous new herbal combination that people could not obtain due to some government regulation?

From the desert of Northern Mexico where he lived in a run down farm with pigs and chickens, he learned how to be slim and agile, even to a hundred years of age.

Later, as he walked down the streets of Argentina visiting the favorite spots of Evita Peron, his companion would tell him stories of miracles performed with medicine from the bark of a tree. He saw hundreds of trees, all of the same family, yet only one had the chemical ingredients necessary for good health.

He wept as he told Jason of evil people around the world, selling bark from "useless trees" and making big money. Jason told him that in America alone, whole companies had sprung up doing just that.

Manila Philippines

Life On A Mountain Of Filth

Over 20,000 professional scavengers pick through the garbage dump known as Smokey Mountain in Manila. They make about $3.00 per day looking for something worth selling on the streets. The working conditions, however, are probably the worst to be found anywhere The air is full of burning rubbish, the heat is unbearable, and the whole place smells like rotten eggs.

When one child was asked how she could stand the smell, she looked surprised and said, 'What smell?" Whole families spend all day up to their knees in filth and rotting garbage and at nights they lay their heads on more rubbish, just waiting for trucks to bring mare decaying filth for them to pick through.

Some families have built paper and cardboard shacks to live in, but they refuse to go too far from the dump, in case they miss a new truckload.

Germs, bacteria and disease are just three of the things these families are exposed to on a daily basis, but they do not seem to get sick. Take a person from America or England and expose them to such a life and I am sure they would become very ill within days.

These people have immune systems so strong that they can live in the world's very worst conditions and survive.

We are, at present, investigating their diet and attitude, which must have a bearing on their good health. It just goes to prove, says Dr. Justin, that our work with herbs, trying to improve the immune system of the world, is really a very worthwhile endeavor.

Africa

Herb Number One

It was July 1982, in a small village in Central Africa. All of the adult villagers had gone from their dome-shaped huts and only the teenage girls were left to take care of the children and babies.

The villagers had travelled 20 miles to a small area surrounded on three sides by high grassy hills. The highest being about 1,200 feet. From its side poured a stream of sparkling, crystal-clear water. Here they made camp and soon the festival of "Devil Be Gone" began.

For three days they would chant, sing and dance. No food would they eat except a strange plant and the only drink would be the water from the spring. By the time they returned to their village, all spots and blemishes would have disappeared, all illness would have vanished, replaced by energy and enthusiasm.

This festival has taken place for centuries and small mention of it was made in Ryder Haggard's book on Africa. The herb consumed is Xpapa.

Investigation showed Xpapa to be an extreme blood builder, a nourishing substance that inhibits the growth of unfriendly bacteria.

It is my belief that if a person purifies the blood, then oxygen and nutrition can travel to every cell, nourishing and building every part of the body.

Nourish and purify your body and I believe that illness goes scurrying. It certainly does with these African villagers.

The pure water they drink at this time also helps to flush away toxins released from the body.

Let's face it. God did not just throw us down here and say, "There's 10,000 fast food restaurants, have fun." He gave us an immune system to take care of poisons and disease. Today, however, our bodies are so toxic that we need to detoxify on a daily basis. God placed herbs on every continent to do just that.

Modern medicine may fight it. They may choose to disregard the 23 times herbs for health are mentioned in the Bible.

They may ignore Hippocrates when he said to all the student doctors, "You Must Use Herbs For Medicine." But the thinking person will not ignore the words of Buddha, Krishna, Bahaji Uhia and Jesus.

England

Herb Number Two—Inula Relenium Compositae

There is probably more bronchitis, asthma, emphysema and other lung problems in England, Scotland, Eire and Wales than anywhere else in the world.

The climate is almost always damp and cold. I have seen Englishmen in Brighton Sussex sitting on the stoney beach, wrapped in blankets, with red faces and runny noses, yet determined to "enjoy" their day at the beach. Cold houses without central heating usually just have fireplaces that cook one side of a person, while the other side freezes. No wonder cold medicine and breathing aides are top sellers there.

When Dr. Ralph Perry-Brown left the hospital for home, he was depressed, to say the least. His colleagues had put him through every test and had tried every medicine, all to no avail. He had emphysema and nothing would help.

He could not practice his profession any more for the slightest movement put him completely out of breath and for the next few minutes he would go through a gasping hell, trying to stabilize himself. From now on an oxygen tank must always be close by. He was furious. He had so much work to do and he was not old...52 is not old...he would shout to himself.

The worst thing about him, however, was his closed mind. He just refused to believe that help could come from any other direction than from the medical profession. "After all," he would think, "the elasticity is gone from my lungs, they can't expand and contract any more and nothing can help that."

There has been a profession in existence since earliest recorded history. It's been known by different names, Witch Doctor, Healer, Naturopath, Homeopath, Herbalist, each with their own beliefs, but mainly the same idea.

One day, while reading a healthy living magazine, Dr. Perry-Brown gazed in amazement at an article stating that the royal family had their own herbalist doctor. The article was complete with a photograph of the Queen Mother and a Doctor Blackie whom, the article explained, had taken care of the royal family for many years.

Now it must be remembered that Dr. Perry-Brown is an Englishman. It is not easy to change an Englishman's mind once he has made it up. But after all, he reasoned, "What's good enough for the Queen is good enough for me," and so he went under Dr. Blackie's care.

The very first thing she did for him was to administer a colon cleanser to make sure he went to the bathroom regularly. The second thing was to give him **Inula Helenium Compositae,** (Elcampane) twice each day.

Special Report: Feb. 1984, Zurich

Elcampane is beneficial for all pulmonary and catarrhal infections. Its sodium phosphate cleans the liver and digestive organs. The potassium chloride dissolves the fibrinous exudations and mucoid matter, and its calcium chlorine supports, feeds and tones the heart muscles. It is a stimulant, a relaxant and a tonic to the mucous membrane (a warming, strengthening, cleansing and toning agent to the gastric, alvine and pulmonary membranes). Because of its powerful healing action and efficient expectoration of pulmonary muscles, herbalists have considered this agent excellent for tuberculosis. It promptly clears up old chronic diseases of the lungs and chest. This herb is the richest source of insulin (a carbohydrate).

The Benefits

In "**Agins Book of Ancient Herbs**," it states: This herb has proven excellent in the following:

Coughs, Asthma, Bronchitis, Pulmonary Complaints, Dyspepsia, Acute Catarrhal Infection, Tuberculosis, Snake Bites, Cyspnea or Shortness of Breath, Wheezing, Cystitis Skin Diseases, all forms of Inflammations, Putrid Sores, Cankers, Skin Rash, Tooth Decay, Whooping Cough, Dropsy, Diphtheria, Kidney and Bladder Stones, Retention of Urine, Delayed Menstruation, Amenorrhea, Phthisis, Vesical Catarrh, Sluggish Liver, Kidney Problems, Bowel Problems, Ulcers, Malnutrition, Rickets, Glandular Insufficiency, Nervous Debility and Muscular Weakness.

To say that Dr. Ralph Perry-Brown is the picture of health today would not be true. But he did not die back in 1977 as they thought he might—emphysema places a great burden on the heart—he can now breathe comfortably and live without oxygen tanks. He can go for walks and he enjoys life. He certainly can talk about herbs (and he constantly does, much to the chagrin of his friends in the local pub).

India

Private Willer had been captured. His regiment, The Bellingham Dragoons, had just marched through the famous Khyber Pass in Northern India when it happened.

He soon found himself riding horseback, surrounded by Indian Revolutionaries, the roughest, dirtiest group he had ever seen. He couldn't believe how fast it had all happened. One minute they were marching double file, leading their horses, when the vicious attack took place. The bag piper, always at the head of the column, had been playing "Road To The Isles" but quickly switched to "On Guard." The next thing Private Willer knew was that a searing pain shot through his shoulder and he became unconscious. When he came to he had been captured and was the only prisoner. Many of his captors had been injured too. A rough bandage had been pushed into the bullet hole in his shoulder and tied tightly. He was not bleeding.

The year was 1918 and most Indians wanted freedom from England which had been their unwanted lord and master for too long. Now was the rebellion, the great uprising. A few days later they arrived at the town of Allahabad. When the townsfolk saw the injured men and worn out horses, they rushed out in the field to pick a mild-smelling grass. Not only were the sick and injured fed the washed grass, but their wounds were wrapped in it also...

It gave instant strength to all. Private Wilier thought that this was a miracle. Even he, standing alone in the prison compound, was given ample "Healing Grass," as the Indians called it. His guard, however, had the bad habit of spitting into everything before he fed it to the Englishman. The guard would then laugh uproariously, calling him an "English pig."

Within one week, Willer's wound had healed and he had to admit that physically he felt better than any time in his life. Of course, the thought of being taken out and shot at any moment put a little damper on his gusto. He had also noticed that once the tired, weak and some injured horses were unleashed from their halters, they would also head to the healing grass. He had watched them race over acres of green, long grass to reach the darker healing grass. There they would graze all day.

When, after 62 days, the English came to Allahabad, the rebels left Willers to his own devices and they fled to the hills. Willers said that he could have kissed his sergeant when he came marching into the prison compound, but decided not to. True, he wanted to get out of the army and return to England, but he certainly did not want to be "ushered out" because of that.

Willers spoke of the healing grass to the British Medical officer. The doctor was well aware of it and, serving in India for many years, he was able to tell many stories about it. "All Indian doctors use it," he said, "and lots of it is shipped on the backs of donkeys to far off Tibet."

This seemed incredible to Willers, for Tibet was the highest country in the world. The donkeys would have to climb narrow trails for weeks on end, just to deliver grass. "Most of it is shipped to monasteries and used for medicine. It is a most hazardous and dangerous journey," the medical officer continued.

When Private Willers did finally get out of the army, and returned to Brighton England, he always made sure that he had a supply of Gotu Kola, the healing grass. For he had studied and found that it was good for all the following:

Mental Fatigue, Age Spots, Ageing, Brain Problems, Lack of Energy, Poor Endurance, High Blood Pressure, Poor Memory, Pituitary Problems, Senility, Menopause, Vitality.

It is now used around the world. The Ultimate Formula contains just the right amount for daily use.

AUSTRALIA

In Sydney, Australia a man dropped down in the street with extreme heart pains. An ambulance was called right away. A lady from a nearby house had watched the incident and calmly walked out, leaning over the man, placed a pillow under his head. Then she gave him a spoonful of liquid Cayenne.

Within three minutes the man got up and walked away, his pain completely gone. The policeman on the spot was flabbergasted at such a speedy recovery from such a severe attack. The ambulance men in turn were furious that their customer had escaped. There was even brief talk about charging the lady with practicing medicine without a license, but they did not pursue this.

It seems that a clinic in New South Wales specializes in manufacturing Cayenne liquid and has been busy using it for all kinds of physical problems for years.

Cayenne has been used for centuries to fight colds, to make a person stronger, to purify the blood, to stop internal bleeding and so much more.

Cayenne has been traced back as far as the Roman Empire where the soldiers, often living in adverse conditions, would take a small pinch of it with a glass of wine each day. They came from sunny Italy only to find themselves living in tents in damp and rainy England or Northern France.

Cayenne is quoted as being the most valuable herb in treating these men. It seems to have a warming effect and proved invaluable in the relieving of breathing problems.

During the Civil War in America, military doctors found that Cayenne would slow down and often stop internal bleeding.

Dr. Malcolm Rae, one of England's top Radionics doctors, told me that the administration of Cayenne to a person feeling lowly or depressed seemed to have a lifting effect, placing a person in a better frame of mind.

Dr. H. Lee of Kowloon, Hong Kong, one of the top herbalists, states that for 40 years he has prescribed Cayenne for all his patients regardless of their complaints because, in his own words, "It simply makes everyone feel better."

As it is my practice to tell the bad along with the good, I feel obligated to mention a funny little fellow that I once knew in Western Australia. Although he was married with children, he had girl friends in every town and city. Although in his 40s, he had the stamina of a horse, even though he wasn't much over five feet tall and weighed hardly 140 lbs. Every night while he was travelling, he was chasing girls.

He thoroughly enjoyed his life-style and felt great all the time. He could stay up all night with some beauty yet be wide awake and ready for work the next day. When his friends would ask him just how he did it, he would smile with a devilish twinkle in his eye and simply say, "Cayenne."

I do know that the right kind of Cayenne, mixed with certain herbs, will make a noticeable difference to the way most people feel.

PSADAS ARGENTINA

Mrs. Torila had been in and out of the hospital many times since giving birth to her sixth child. Something had happened to her during that birth. Her bladder was now weak, she had kidney trouble and complained constantly of back pains.

For two and a half years she had been on pain killers, but she was now afraid she was getting immune to them, for even the strongest ones did not seem to work any more.

Not only that but the side-effects made her drowsy, irritable and anxious. Thank goodness that her eldest child could take care of the younger ones.

Life was not worth anything to Gia Torila and she quite often prayed to Mary, Mother of Christ, to let her leave this pain and suffering. Yet another operation was scheduled to remove more kidney stones and she dreaded it with all her heart. It was then that she read the book, "In Search of the Perfect Cleanse" and, as she says, "The following chapter changed my life:"

Your Weakness And Your Herb According To Your Birth Sign

LIBRA

The Complaints Of Libra Are: Kidney Stones, Pains In The Back, Bladder Problems And Over Acidity. Libras' Healing Herb Is Burdock

These were all the things Gia was suffering from. Coincidence? No, I don't think so, for since I published this list back in May 1984, I have received hundreds of letters from astounded people, all stating that the chart was 100 percent accurate.

Mrs. Gia Torila could not find burdock in her own country so she ordered some from an herbalist in England. The results, according to her, have been spectacular.

She is now leading a normal life without pain and painkillers. Her frame of mind is good—she enjoys life and she has more energy and enthusiasm than most of her friends.

Herb Number Six - Herbalene

"This herb will heal you," the old lady in Singapore told me. "Not only that, but it will bring into line the physical, spiritual and mental body so that they have perfect balance."

She told me this in 1977, while I searched in desperation for something to help me live after many doctors had given me up for dead.

And when I was better I was told, "It's an amazing thing we have found Jason," Dr. Ian Pierce explained. "We all know that red clover is a great blood purifier, the same as chaparral, but when you mixed them together with herbalene it acted as a catalyst and made the two herbs 27 times stronger. That is why you lived." Dr. Ian Pierce is a famous English Doctor who tested these herbs completely.

Imagine, if you will, the herbs you have just read about, mixed in exact proportions, then added to herbalene, The

Great Catalyst (called our "special spice") for the past six months many people have been using this "Ultimate Formula," including myself. It is in capsule form. We have different people taking different doses. For instance, 20 people have been taking two capsules daily. Another 20 have been taking three capsules daily. Twenty more have been taking six capsules daily.

Although all benefited immensely from the doses, it was found that three each day is ample.

Varicose veins in one lady disappeared. A few cases of hemorrhoids vanished, asthmatics noticed a lessening of tightness and wheezing in the chest.

(I have always thought that asthma was an emotional problem so I personally feel that the people felt better because they were able to relax and rid themselves of stress.)

A neurotic person claimed he felt better and was more stable. He did not worry so much about himself, his appearance, what he would wear and was able to relax more socially.

We call this combination of herbs the "Ultimate Combination" because we feel that it is just that. Individually the herbs are effective, taken as a group they cover a greater spectrum of illnesses. Mixed with the catalyst herbalene, they are dynamite.

The tropical plant world is an absolute and inexhaustible source for modern medicine. The World Resources Institute in America proclaims that at least one modern medicine out of every four comes from herbs from the Tropical Rain forests.

They also claim that "There are at least 1,400 tropical plants that are potential treatments for cancer." This information from "*Voice of Nature,*" Aug. 1988, Jakarta.

This writer has been well aware of the fact that many herbs can serve the same purpose in treating a specific illness. The problem is finding the most effective. Therefore, some herbs mentioned herein have been substituted by others proven to be even more effective in treating the same malady.

THE ANGEL

I walked into the hospital ward with considerable anxiety. We had driven 40 miles to visit the cripple children's home and it was such a grey, drab building and such a grey, drab day that I felt sorry for the kids even before we entered.

One ward was full of children, all lying on their small beds. Many had no arms and legs, they had been born that way. Some were Mongoloids and others had heads so large that they could not lift them. All were under 12 years of age.

One of the little girls, however, was running around, from one bed to another, talking to all the children happily, giggling and laughing. The children that could not move were happy just watching her. She was a bright child with blonde curls and I guessed that she was about 10 years old.

When she came over to meet me I noticed that she had no arms and was also blind in one eye. The nurse whispered that she had been born that way.

She was radiant and her blue eyes sparkled. She told me she had new shoes on and looked down at the cheap blue canvas shoes with elastic over the instep instead of laces.

I asked her what made her so happy and she replied, "I can run anywhere, sometimes I go on a walk all around the hospital, I am so happy. God has been good to me. Some of these children can't even get out of bed, but I can go anywhere."

I hugged her to me and looked once again at the cheap canvas shoes. On the drive home, with a lump still in my throat, I remembered losing my temper just the day before when I couldn't get a taxi and had to walk about 20 blocks to my hotel.

THE AUTHENTIC FACE OF JESUS

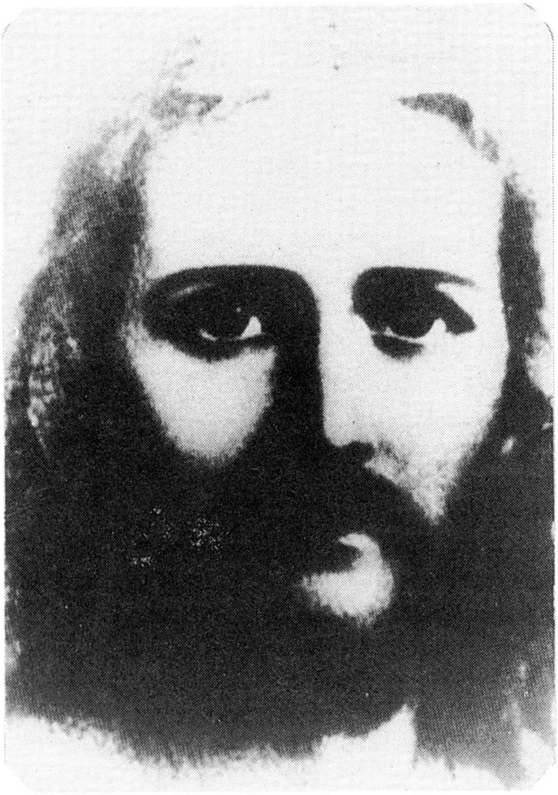

An English couple went to Puttaparthi. The husband had faith in Baba but the wife believed in Jesus Christ. Baba called them for an interview. The wife felt embarrassed because she believed in Jesus and was now with another spiritual guide. The husband had an automatic camera which started clicking by itself during the interview. When the couple went back to England and had the film developed, they got this picture of the face of Jesus.

On their next journey to Puttaparthi, Baba called them for another interview and asked them whether they liked the picture. He then told them that this was a picture of Jesus Christ at the age of 28 or 29 when he left India to return to Jerusalem. Baba cleared the wife's doubts and proved that All Forms are His own Forms.

Chapter 23

Meanwhile - In Great Britain

Integrated Health Care

How The Foundation for Integrated Medicine is Bringing Together Orthodox Medicine and Complementary Therapies

The Foundation for Integrated Medicine, a charity initiated at the suggestion of His Royal Highness the Prince ofWales, has as its purpose the comprehensive integration of complementary and orthodox medicines. This will be achieved by the attainment of the following objectives:

TO PROMOTE and support scientific research into complementary medical treatments and their integration with orthodox medical treatments;
TO PROVIDE educational programs and training support for doctors, nurses and therapists in integrated medicine;
TO PROMOTE wider awareness of the clinical and economic benefits of effective integrated health and medical practices, both among health care professionals and in the wider community;
TO COLLECT, codify, disseminate and thereby protect the knowledge of complementary medical practices and treatments for the benefit of future generations of practitioners;
TO COLLABORATE with other medical and complementary organizations thus benefiting from all sources of knowledge.

The Goals Of Integrated Health Care

A good health care system is much more than a means of keeping people alive for longer. It must:

- Promote health and well being in addition to treating illness;
- Deal with people as whole individuals, obtaining Their confidence and trust, and building inner strength for the treatment of their illness;
- Restore to people their feeling of self-worth and esteem through active participation in their own treatment, which is often essential for recovery.

Drawing Upon The World's Experience

Over the centuries, vast experience has been gained all over the world from the use of traditional treatments. Some of these treatments will now be researched by the Foundation so that the benefits can be enjoyed by people everywhere. This will lead to wider acceptance and greater use.

Limitations In Our Existing Health Care System

Modern medicine has achieved outstanding results. However, there are increasing limitations and escalating costs. There are now real fears that the demands being placed upon conventional health services may generate burdens which could prove impossible to meet. There is also concern about the potential side effects of treatment. More could be achieved in our health care system, and often at a lower cost, if effective complementary therapies were integrated with existing practice.

Existing health care systems are experiencing growing difficulty in addressing 20th Century illnesses, many of which are due to the affects of modern society. This is where the integration of orthodox and complementary medicine can really help.

The Role Of Scientific Research

The objectives of the Foundation for Integrated Medicine are to research complementary medical practices and their integration with orthodox medical treatments. Cost benefit analysis and the efficacy of treatments will be of prime importance.

The research program will be the responsibility of the Research Committee comprised of eminent members of the professions with extensive experience in treatment and research. The outcome of research studies will be subject to independent analysis.

Results So Far

The first pilot research study is nearing completion at a major London Teaching Hospital. The willingness of a unit there to collaborate in this research reflects the interest shown in integrated medicine by one of the most orthodox of establishments, with a worldwide reputation for leading medical research.

CASE STUDY

This year-old baby girl caught an infection while on holiday abroad with her parents when she was five months old, which led to congestion of her immune system.

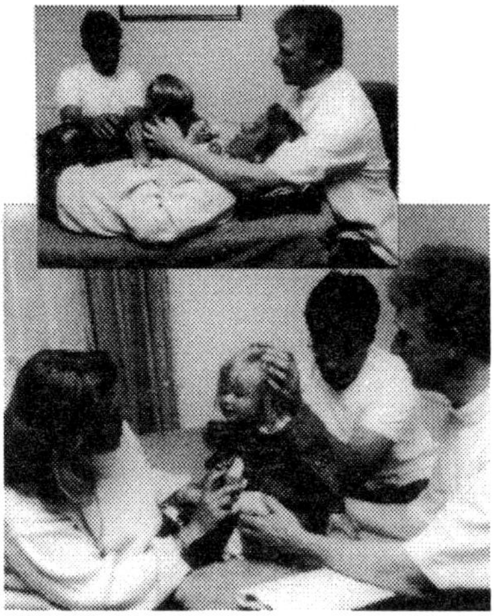

Since then she had suffered from recurring ear and bowel infections, tonsillitis, vomiting and general lethargy - although the original infection had been successfully treated. Her mother was told of the benefits of cranial osteopathy, and took her to registered osteopaths who had received postgraduate training with the Osteopathic Centre for Children. Their treatment enabled her to recover fully by helping the drainage within the body to flow naturally, and in this way enhancing her immune system.

• •

CASE STUDY

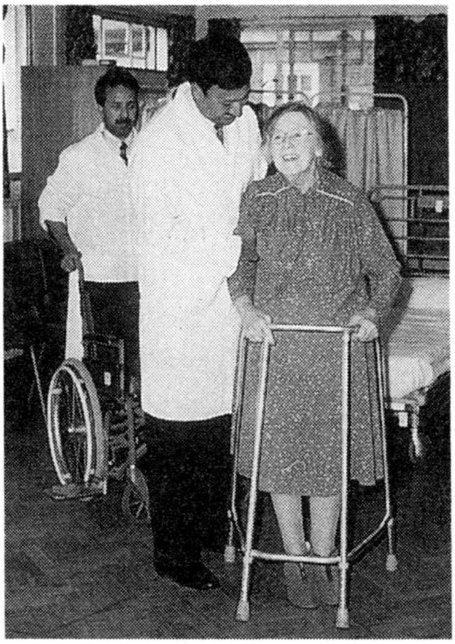

One of the elderly patients at a major London teaching hospital who has benefited from Marma therapy, an ancient form of deep neuromuscular massage which has been used for physical and rehabilitation therapy in India for several centuries.

Clinical observation suggests that the massage works by increasing blood flow into the affected groups of muscles, as well as by directly improving muscle tone. It is also believed to improve the flow of information between the muscles and the brain, in this way helping the brain to "re-learn" how to control the muscles after brain damage, such as a stroke.

CASE STUDY

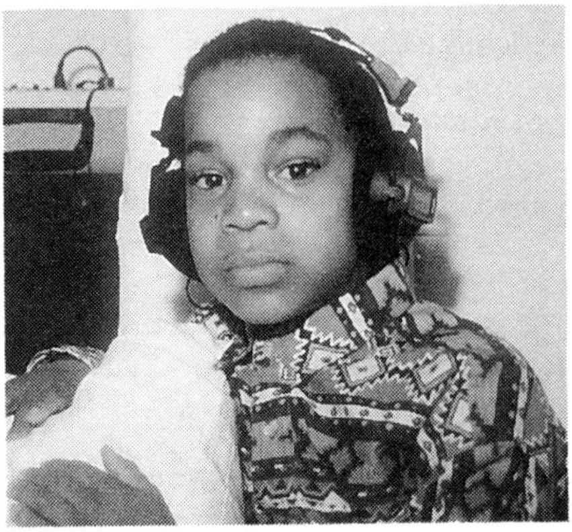

This child listens attentively to specially chosen music through headphones on spe-cifically designed equipment, for 30 minutes twice a day, as part of a 10-day course of treatment which includes counseling and other training.

The treatment can help with disorders such as learning disabilities, dyslexia, and attention deficit disorder.

The first study is examining the sue of neuromuscular massage techniques—Marma therapy—derived from traditional Indian health care, for the rehabilitation of elderly patients who have had strokes. Early results from this study are promising and planning is underway for a further multi-centre, large scale study.

We have come this far with the aid of generous private donations. We are now in a position to make real progress in achieving the objectives set out in this document.

Initial Research Program

These are the first fully-costed research projects planned by the Foundation,

Rehabilitation For Stroke Patients

(Two Clinical Trials Are Being Planned)

Late Stroke Rehabilitation

This trial will build upon the Foundation's pilot study of marma therapy, the ancient Indian neuromuscular massage technique. A multi-centre randomized-controlled trial is being planned for 1995/6. This will assess the efficiency of Marma therapy in late stroke rehabilitation of people who have had a stroke at least 6 months previously and who have gained the maximum recovery possible using NHS rehabilitation techniques.

The trial will require a research team that includes a research registrar, Marma therapist, physiotherapist, exercise therapist and an independent assessor of patient outcome. (Projected Cost - 360,000)

Acute Stroke Rehabilitation

There is considerable anecdotal evidence that acupuncture can have significant effect on recovery from stroke in the acute phase (i.e., within the first 3 months after a stroke). A recently published clinical trial in Sweden provides further evidence of this, but the results require confirmation with larger, most sophisticated multi-centre randomized-controlled trials. Both Marma therapy and acupuncture will be evaluated. (Projected Cost - 280,000)

National Audit For Herbal Medicine

There are around 300 herbal practitioners who are members of the National Institute of Medical Herbalists (NIMH). Preliminary work has begun to establish a national network for clinical audit and research. A clinical information analyst is now required for 3 years, to design and implement a computerized database. This will be used by individual practitioners and local groups to audit their clinical practice. It will also be used by the NIMH as a means of monitoring nationally the use of herbs for particular conditions, for assessing outcomes of herbal medical practice, and for more detailed research projects. (Projected Cost - 185,000 over 3 years)

National Audit For Acupuncture

There is a need to aid development of the profession of acupuncturists and to spread knowledge of their work. Therefore a national service is to be developed:

- to design an audit system (software, materials and a training package) which will support acupuncturists in their clinical work;
- to establish a database of treatments and outcome which will influence policy and aid development of the profession.

The project will be carried out in collaboration with the professional acupuncturists organizations. (Projected Cost - 175,000 over 3 years)

Other Research Projects Under Consideration:

- Bronchial Asthma in children
- Chronic Brain Injury
- Management of Irritable Bowel Syndrome
- Improvement in Function of Autistic and Learning-Disabled Children
- Chronic Back Pain
- Acute Cardiac Illness
- Epilepsy
- Evaluation of Different Models of Delivering Integrated Medicine
- Examination of Techniques used for Diagnosis in Complementary Medicine
- Identification of Users of Complementary Medicine who would benefit from the availability of an Integrated Medical Service
- Evaluation of Different Delivery Methods of Integrated Medical Services

Outline costs for these projects are on the order of 2.5 million. The initial research projects will cost 1 million. (Total Costs - 3.5 million)

THE BOARD OF THE FOUNDATION

A small Board will oversee the policy and management of the Foundation.

Hugh van Cutsem, *Chairman of the Board*
Keith Bayliss, *Director, Kleinwort Benson*
Dr. Peter Fenwick, *Institute of Psychiatry, The Maudsley Hospital*
Ian Marks CBE, *Chairman of the Aim Foundation*
Professor Richard Petty, *University of Pennsylvania*
The Rt. Hon. The Baroness Rawlings

For further information, please contact: The Foundation for Integrated Medicine, 7th Floor, Windsor House, 83 Kingsway, London WC2B6SD. Telephone: 01712423355. Registered charity number: 1026800.

An Open Letter From Prince Charles

There are few things more satisfying than to see an idea that one truly believes in take hold. When the motivation behind the idea is to help others, the sense of satisfaction is all the deeper.

I am convinced that the integration of complementary and orthodox medical practices is urgently needed. It is all about breaking down artificial barriers of geography, culture and education so that we can bring the sum of human knowledge and experience to bear in caring even better for those who suffer from ill health or disability.

The Foundation for integrated Medicine has already begun to produce outstanding results through early trials. These merely hint at what is possible given adequate funding. Perhaps the most exciting aspect is the potential to improve patient car whilst making more effective use of scarce and costly resources. Integrated medicine thus addresses constructively the most fundamental dilemma facing health care today and into the new century.

The Foundation has my full personal commitment and support.

H.R.H. PRINCE CHARLES

I have recently received a registered letter from Prince Charles. The contents are as follows:

Dear Sir Jason,

I felt enormously heartened and touched to read your kind letter recently. How wonderful that you have indeed survived since I last saw you and I am most grateful that you think it may have been something to do with me! I too have been trying my best to bring the orthodox practitioners together with the complementary therapists and, after nine years of effort, a bill to regulate osteopathy was passed through Parliament last year as a result. I hope we can now make progress with homeopathy and acupuncture ...

We have also established recently a Foundation for Integrated Medicine with the object of integrating the best of clinical with the best of complementary, or traditional, medicine. We have plans for conducting research projects with various hospital departments in the UK, but we need £3 million to maintain the necessary integrated research. Do you know anyone in the USA who might be interested in helping with the funding?!

Yours sincerely, Charles

Letter From America's Leading Herbalist & Nutritionist:
The Most Famous Bernard Jensen Writes:

BERNARD JENSEN INTERNATIONAL

Dear Jason,

You have been a special person in my life and an inspiration and it's a wonderful thing to be able to work In the same field together helping people to be in the best of health.

I certainly want to wish you the very finest and I got your address from Mr. Lowder who was here the other day and we had quite a talk about you.

With all best wishes and sending my best greetings I remain...

Sincerely yours,

Dr. Bernard Jensen

Sir Jason Winters Realizes Astounding Worldwide Success Surprises the Medical Field, Governments and Natural Health Advocates

- Over 12 million books have been sold.
- Received Award of Merit from a United States Congressman.
- Over 62 million people worldwide have used the Jason Winters' products.
- Received Knighthood in Malta.
- 1993 tour of Asia was a great success. Thousands attended his lectures, which were shown on national television.
- Given Medal of Honor in Madrid.
- Laureate of Belgum-Netherlands and South Africa.
- Has won awards from seven different foreign governments.
- Products are now used in 70 countries throughout the world.
- Featured in over 100 health magazines.
- Famous Author, Ruth Montgomery, devoted an entire chapter to Jason Winters in her top selling book *Threshold to Tomorrow.*
- The formulas have been mentioned by dozens of authors throughout the world.
- Sir Jason Winters wants to make it clear that we do not recommend the rejection of orthodox methods of treating illness. If you are ill, see your doctor immediately. Tell your doctor that you will do everything that he or she sees fit to help you. Also ask your doctor if it is okay to change your eating habits, your way of thinking and to take herbs. Any thinking doctor should have no problem with this.
- The objective of Sir Jason Winters is to get all of the healing arts, both orthodox and unorthodox, to work together for the benefit of mankind.
- Sir Jason follows the instructions that Prince Charles stated at the grand opening of the Bristol Clinic. "We must work together to help our fellow man."
- Sir Jason does not believe that herbs cure any illness, but he has been assured by many herbalists that they do "strengthen the body and then the body can help itself." This is referred to in the Bible and by Buddha, Krishna and Hippocrates. This is why 150 of the top prescription medicines come from herbs. Medical prescriptions written by doctors everyday in the United States and England, as well as many other countries, contain herbs.

References and Suggested Further Reading

1 By the editors of Prevention Magazine Health Books, *The Complete Book of Natural & Medicinal Cures,* Rodale Press, Emmaus, Pennsylvania © 1994.
2. Your Choice - The database for Vitamins, Minerals & Herbs © 1961 AM Unlimit Naples, FL
3. Ody, Penelope, *The Complete Medicinal Herbal,* London, N.Y., Stuttgart, Dorling Kindersicy ©1993.
4. Tenney. Louise. *Today's" Herbal Health,* 2nd ed. Woodland Books ©1983.
5. Mairesse, Michelle, *The health Secrets of Medicinal Herbs,* N.Y., Arco Publishing ©1981.
6. Castleman, Michael, *The Healing Herbs,* Rodale Press, Penn. ©1991.
7. Blacow, N.W. *Martindale Extra Pharmucopeola,* 26th ed. London: Pharmaceutical Press ©1974.
8. Claus, EP. and Tyler, V.B., *Pharmocognosy,* 5th ed. Lea and Febiger ©1965.
9. Kadans, J.M. *Modern Encyclopedia of Herbs,* West Nyack, N.Y.: Parker Publishing Co. ©l974
10. Osol, A. and Farrar C , *The Dispensatory of the United States of America,* 25th ed. Philadelphia: J P. Lippincott Co. ©l975.
II. Bouchey, G.D and Gjerstad, G., "Chemical Studies of Aloe Vera Juice II." *Quartz J. Crude Drug Res* 9 (4)1445-53.
12. Cheney, R.H.. Aloe Drug in Human Therapy, "Quart *J Crude Drug Res 10* (I): 1523-30.
13. Grieve. M.A., *Modern Herbal,* N.Y.: Hefner Publishing © 1959.
14. Harrington, H.D., *Edible Native Plants of the Rocky Mountains,* Albuquerque; University of New Mexico Press, ©1967.
15. Der Marderosian, A., Medical Teas-Boon or Bane?" Drug *Therapy,* ©1977.
16. Arena, J.M., *Poisoning - Toxicology: Symptoms and Treatments,* 3rd ed. Springfield, Ill: Charles C. Thomas ©1976.
17. Macht, DI. and Cook, H.M., *J Am Pharm Ass,* 1932, 324.
18. Mindell, Earl, R.Ph., Ph.D., *Earl Mindells Herb Bible.,* Published by Simon & Schuster N.Y., ©1992
19. Mairesse, Michelle, *The Health Secrets* Of *Medicinal Herbs,* N.Y., Arco Publishing. Inc. ©1981.
20. Kloss, Jethro, *Back to Eden,* Back to Eden Books Publishing Co,, Loma Linda, CA. ©1988.
21. Mabey, R., *The New Age Herbalist.* Macmillan Publishing Co., N.Y., N.Y. 1988.
22. Winters, Jason, *Killing Cancer,* Vinton Publishing of Las Vegas. NV. 1980.
23 Graf, A.B., *Exotic Plant Manual,* Roehrs Company, H. Rutherford, New Jersey. 1974
24. Tyler, V.E., Ph.D, *The Honest Herbal,* Pharmaceutical Products Press. 1993.
25. Balch, James F., MD; Balch, Phyllis R., CNC, *Prescriptions for Natural Healing,* Very Publishing Group, Inc., Garden City Park, NY.
26. Montgomery, Ruth, Threshold 'To Tomorrow. The Ballantine Publishing Group, Fawcetti Crest, NY

List of books that mentioned Sir Jason Winters and/or the herbal tea.

Threshold to Tomorrow, Ruth Montgomery—Random House
Unlimited Power, Tony Roberts — Fawcet
Prescription for Natural Healing, James & Phyllis Balch—Avery
Helping Yourself with Natural Healing, Lewis Harrison—Prentice
Herbs Fighting Cancer, Romeo Ticson
Cancer Battle Plan, Anne E. Frahm—Pinon Press
Integrated Healthcare, Josef De Ubaldo—REX Publishing International
More encounters with the unknown, Jaime T. Licauco,—Anvil
Options, the alternative cancer therapy book

on CD Rom

Your Choice Explicitly lists Sir Jason Winters Tea for use in combating Cancer
I.A.M. Unlamented. Inc.

Over 13 Million In Print In Nine Languages

THE JASON WINTERS INTERNATIONAL COLLECTION

Notes

Notes

Notes

Notes

Notes